G. LOWES DICKINSON

A MODERN SYMPOSIUM

With an introductory essay
The Uses of G. Lowes Dickinson

by LOUIS FILLER
Antioch College

FREDERICK UNGAR PUBLISHING CO.
NEW YORK

**MILESTONES
OF THOUGHT**
in the History of Ideas

General Editors
F. W. STROTHMANN
Stanford University
HANS KOHN
City College of New York

THE USES OF G. LOWES DICKINSON

It is a particular pleasure to introduce this work because it involves elements which have been on hard times in recent decades, and to the loss of everyone. I refer not so much to the symposium, which has disappeared into history and is rarely identified with anybody after Plato, but to the essayic style and content. The essay, above all other literary forms, is concerned for the personality of the writer. The refining of phrases for better and more effective communication would seem one of the most challenging and intriguing of tasks. Moreover, essays take brain-power: the ability to concentrate on a line of thought and explore its implications. Can it be that the unpopularity of the essay corresponded to a weakening of public conviction that the individual was important and could influence such vast phenomena as war, the "population explosion," and the competing isms of modern life?—that readers felt that the ideas of individuals, however persuasive, however desirable, had to give place to those of government "task forces" and of "teams" of specialists in the sciences and the arts? The career of the essay may be taken as one barometer of the status of the individual in his battle against Big Brother. However much we may claim to prefer the values of the "free world" over those advocated by totalitarians, it is in the *details* of our lives—in the

way we think as well as act—that we show our real
qualities. The essay illuminates them, and enables us to
reinforce them.

This is not the place to probe fully the meaning of
Dickinson's life and work. G. Lowes Dickinson (1862-
1932) was one of the great humanists of his time, and to
do him justice would require elaborate consideration of
his activities and associations, as well as of his numerous
works. These include studies in modern history and politics,
studies in ancient thought and literature, of which *The
Greek View of Life* (1896) was a distinguished example,
verses, philosophical essays, and religious ponderings. Yet
something must be said of the life and development of the
man who probably invented the phrase, "a League of
Nations," and whose symposium which follows offers so
much insight into Man as a social and political being.

Dickinson was born in London of cultured parentage,
and early exhibited talents as a classical scholar. Though
outstanding in this field at King's College, Cambridge,
he conscientiously undertook to become a physician, in
order to better serve mankind. He finally abandoned that
vocation as unsuited to his temperament, and entered into
the study of modern history for the same generous purpose
as had motivated his concern for medicine. It was as an
historian that Dickinson established himself at King's,
where he became familiar and admired for his lectures and
appealing personal traits. He retired from active academic
life in 1920.

It is difficult to know how best to judge the essays he
prepared before World War I in national and international
characteristics, if only because he can hardly have been
expected to foretell their precise unfoldings. Still note-

worthy are the efforts he made to dig beneath clichés to
the realities of the genius and distinct qualities of races.
In his *Letters from John Chinaman* (1901)—more deli-
cately entitled *Letters from a Chinese Official,* in the
American edition—he sought imaginatively to confront the
West with the viewpoint of the educated Oriental. He even
boldly and evocatively ventured to describe the rugged and
gentle scenes among which the gentleman had been reared in
China, and to which he was loyal. Dickinson, and his Chinese
spokesman, warned the West that it courted disaster in
opening China for crass purposes, and though he did not
foresee Red China and militant atheism, his warnings still
merit re-reading:

> It is the nations of Christendom who have come to us
> to teach us by sword and fire that Right in this world is
> powerless unless it is supported by Might! Oh, do not
> doubt that we shall learn the lesson! . . . You are arming
> a nation of four hundred million! a nation which, until
> you came, had no better wish than to live at peace with
> themselves and all the world. . . .

In 1912, Dickinson became the first recipient of the
Albert Kahn Traveling Fellowship; the result was his
An Essay on the Civilizations of India, China, and Japan.
Dickinson was emphatically concerned for civilization,
rather than material progress, and it was thus not un-
expected that he should have included in his essay criti-
cisms of the United States, which he had twice toured as
a lecturer, and which then troubled him by its too-easy
confidence, its tendency toward superficiality. It continues
to be his searching and objective intentions, rather than
the precise accuracy of his conclusions, which first com-

pels appreciation. Whether, as Dickinson claimed, the spirit of India was essentially religious, that of China first of all "human," can be controverted. Yet much that Dickinson observes and remarks appeals to the heart and mind as true. The reader is stimulated to agree and to disagree, and above all to think.

Dickinson saw very clearly in Japan the mighty struggle which was going on between its feudalistic supporters and its proponents of modernity, who together constituted a threat to the West. Unfortunately, he better perceived the competition between East and West than he did that competition which was soon to throw the West itself into the earth-shaking convulsion which is enigmatically known as World War I.

Dickinson's contribution to the thinking which accompanied that fateful era is without doubt the most controversial aspect of his career. There can be no question of his sincere desire to understand the roots of the conflict and to contribute to the organization of a League of Nations which would make another such conflict impossible. His *The European Anarchy* (1916) recognized Great Britain's long imperialistic past, as well as Germany's more modern efforts in that direction. Yet a close reading of Dickinson's review of British and Continental history makes clear his belief that, whatever his own country's errors and faults in the past, it was Germany which had taken the step which had brought on the war, it was the German government which had to bear the primary responsibility for the catastrophe. Thus, Dickinson's very sincerity, his patent ability to weigh factors with apparent dispassionateness, served the British war effort. Unlike the manifest English propagandists, Dickinson stood before the world with clean hands. And his call for a League of Nations provided the one slogan which could justify American entrance into the war, as it eventually did.

It seems only fair to emphasize Dickinson's honorable intentions; in *The Choice Before Us* (1917), he not only hailed America's entry into the war, but expressed his satisfaction that the American decision had "no other purpose than to secure the rule of right." He denounced, in *Causes of International War* (1920), the opportunism which permitted Lloyd George to maintain power in Great Britain by appealing to popular prejudice with his "Hang the Kaiser!" slogan. Dickinson was totally and explicitly opposed to the shallow greediness of the Allies which disfigured the Versailles settlement. As with Woodrow Wilson, his eloquence in favor of peace and international justice was real and perceptive. His disillusionment with the treaty-makers, and with a public which was "jazzing, and racing and mobbing Mary Pickford," as he bitterly phrased it, was unqualified.

His *The International Anarchy, 1904-1914* (1926), a rich, fulsome, varied account, is one of the best books on the subject: his testament, addressed to the young, and, he hoped, through them, to larger audiences. But Dickinson returned with relief to his studies in more ancient lore, though, to his mind, they bore upon his own times. His dialogue between Plato and "a modern young man," *After Two Thousand Years* (1931), is one of his most stimulating and creative efforts, and probes the meaning of Good and roads to an ideal Republic with practiced skill.

Fortunately for us, as David Graham Phillips once put it, we are not so weak as our weaknesses, but as strong as our strengths. Dickinson's Quixotic search for world peace may interest posterity only in moderation. We prefer to remember people who held out against the current, it seems. Bertrand Russell, Randolph Bourne, Romain Rolland come to memory, rather than Hamilton Holt, James T. Shotwell, and (in this field) Dickinson. But posterity is unlikely to wish to deprive itself of Dickinson's fine learning and understanding. His life-long effort to attain truth resulted in a frame of mind which gave him sympathetic insight into disparate ways of thinking and personalities. He found it a familiar task to concentrate on lines of thought which were not his own. This generalization must be qualified. Dickinson was unprepared for the brutish demagoguery which World War I unleashed, and for the communist and fascist mentalities which it spawned. He cherished ideals of competent and responsible leaders, able and willing to learn, and determined to maintain principles in the face of public clamor. *A Modern Symposium* was his masterpiece in the presentation of such statesmen. It applied his classical training to his historical interests. It displayed such a comparison of political programs as can be found nowhere else, with a felicity of phrase which was Dickinson's own.

It is his catholicity which immediately attracts the eye in *A Modern Symposium*. Where else can one find so much courtesy and mutual respect between fundamental antagonists? The doctrinaire modern mind has found this sentimental, a sign of weakness, of "confused liberalism." The Marxist, the neo-conservative, and similar types have derogated it for being precisely what it is: a product of pre-war political thinking which rested upon literateness and reason, rather than a regard for popular passions. Communists who emphasized social injustice and dialectical materialism, fascists who capitalized on social neuroses found such modes of thought beneath contempt: a species of ineffectual idealism. There is evidence, however, that the attitude of Dickinson and some of his friends may return to general favor. Development of atomic weapons and the dangers they have presented to civilization have thrown doubt on the practicality of cynical and disruptive statesmanship which might have the effect of setting nuclear warheads into motion. Under such conditions, there is new occasion to prefer politicians who seek peace rather than war, and who are able to discern the humanity in their social competitors, at home and abroad.

But all this is far from constituting the whole of Dickinson's achievement. In his symposium he juxtaposes not politicians alone, not only persons who view society and the state in different lights, but men whose views transcend politics. Dickinson assumes that the poet, the journalist, the scientist have talents and represent interests which affect society as surely and as substantially as do those of a conservative or an anarchist. In short, Dickinson sees *people,* rather than pens or programs. It is this emphasis upon the humanity of his protagonists which gives essential life to his symposium. His liberal, Remenham, is more than a Parliamentary position; he is a Darwinian and an anti-Platonist. Allison, the socialist, is a patent Fabian, to whom the brave, new world he anticipates is a problem in technical adjustment of conditions to social needs. It is interesting to note that Dickinson had no reason, in his symposium, to reflect the complex debates among the Russian socialists which were creating what would later be called "Leninism." But it needs to be recalled that their potential was wholly unrealized, even by the debaters themselves. Dickinson tries to recognize the extremist in the person of MacCarthy, the anarchist, whose position he made as reasonable as he knew how.

Dickinson's expositors are not only men of principle; they are representative of interests in society, and they have the gift of loyalty to their own. Their hope is to provide the best accounting for their class abilities and perquisites that conditions may permit. They apologize neither for being rich nor poor; their finances are not subjects of discussion. Dickinson thus reminds us that there was a time when one could have social consequence without necessarily being "successful." This was before the "treason of the intellectuals" too often made them creatures of political trends and personalities: "ghost writers," "proletarian novelists," purveyors of patriotic apologies, and anything but independent spirits.

All the statements of positions which Dickinson displays deserve attention, but there is particular significance in the viewpoint of Wilson, the biologist, representing the scientist's attitude toward man and society. Wilson is unimpressed by the politicians; to his mind, their views are enfeebled by lack of insight into the changing nature of the world, which renders their outlooks obsolete. He finds literature ridiculous: insufficiently concerned for the real. Those who despise the essay must, indeed, join forces with Wilson, for he is of those who find its purposes futile. Science, he asserts, has diminished the significance of the individual; it is only the race which is now important.[1] The advance of the race constitutes progress. But progress is not destined; it must be willed and created. Persons like Wilson "believe neither in a good God directing the

[1] See pages 81 and following.

course of events, nor in a blind power that controls them independently and in despite of human will." Their fate they hold to be in their own hands. They intend to erect a social system which employs breeding and education to produce useful citizens for the state. "Caesar and Napoleon will give place to Comte and Herbert Spencer; and Newton and Darwin sit in judgment on Plato and Aquinas."

There is something prophetic about Dickinson's handling of this significant social type. His vision of the future, says Wilson, "makes us, in a word, what we are, the first of the new generation." It takes little imagination to perceive in this scientist of meagre ethics and philosophy, with contempt for the individual and for the accreted human experiences of thousands of years what C.P. Snow called *The New Man:* men who could create the atomic bomb, but who could contribute little to the creation of a social fabric which could live with it comfortably. Among them would be those who voluntarily handed over atomic secrets to Soviet agents. Similarly, one can take Dickinson's Tory, and Socialist, and, for that matter, his poet and his man of letters, and ask oneself how these types have fared through the years, since Dickinson displayed their opinions before the world. Toryism is long dead; Cantilupe himself freely concedes this. Poetry has suddenly re-emerged as important in the phenomenon of Boris Pasternak; but it has not done so, yet, in Great Britain or the United States. Socialism? Business? Dickinson's most important achievement, in *A Modern Symposium,* was, after all, that he developed a method for assaying social phenomena outside the vulgar pragmatic criteria of apparent workableness and success. He asked, not only that a tendency exist in society, but that it be able to formulate a rationale for its existence which could persuade reasonable men. Our present difficult age demands the most firm and civilized minds of people who desire not only to survive, but to survive with dignity and hope; and in such an age, *A Modern Symposium* does not lose its title to the word "modern." We will not survive if we inadequately unite our forces, inadequately appreciate their content.

Such understanding takes not merely tolerance and attention; it requires a philosophic understanding of the weakness and ephemeral character of the individual—his need for giving due import to first principles. It requires humanity as well as intelligence. Both of these Dickinson mixed with his remarkable grasp of the distinctive qualities which the members of his "club" possessed. His humanity and intelligence lifted Dickinson's prose above common analysis to a plane where words are appropriate because they express the spirit of men, and where they become literature. As one of his speakers puts it[2]:

The dust of oblivion will bury our debates. Something we shall have achieved, but not what we intended. . . . This, at any rate, is the moment of truce. The great arena is empty, the silent benches vanish into the night. Under the glimmer of the moon figures more than mortal haunt the scene of our ephemeral contests. It is they which stand behind us and deal the blows which seem to be ours. When we are laid in the dust they will animate other combatants; when our names are forgotten they will blazon others in perishable gold. Why, then, should

[2]See pages 38-39.

we strive and cry, even now in the twilight hour? The same sky encompasses us, the same stars are above us. What are my opinions, what are Remenham's? Froth on the surface! The current bears all alike along to the destined end. For a moment let us meet and feel its silent, irresistible force; and in this moment reach across the table the hand of peace.

LOUIS FILLER

Antioch College
September, 1962

THE SPEAKERS

LORD CANTILUPE
A TORY

ALFRED REMENHAM
A LIBERAL

REUBEN MENDOZA
A CONSERVATIVE

GEORGE ALLISON
A SOCIALIST

ANGUS MacCARTHY
AN ANARCHIST

HENRY MARTIN
A PROFESSOR

CHARLES WILSON
A MAN OF SCIENCE

ARTHUR ELLIS
A JOURNALIST

PHILIP AUDUBON
A MAN OF BUSINESS

AUBREY CORYAT
A POET

SIR JOHN HARINGTON
A GENTLEMAN OF LEISURE

WILLIAM WOODMAN
A MEMBER OF THE SOCIETY OF FRIENDS

GEOFFRY VIVIAN
A MAN OF LETTERS

A MODERN SYMPOSIUM

SOME of my readers may have heard of a club known as the Seekers. It is now extinct; but in its day it was famous, and included a number of men prominent in politics or in the professions. We used to meet once a fortnight on the Saturday night, in London during the winter, but in the summer usually at the country house of one or other of the members, where we would spend the week end together. The member in whose house the meeting was held was chairman for the evening; and after the paper had been read it was his duty to call upon the members to speak in what order he thought best. On the occasion of the discussion which I am to record, the meeting was held in my own house, where I now write, on the North Downs. The company was an interesting one. There was Remenham, then Prime

Minister, and his great antagonist Mendoza, both of whom were members of our society. For we aimed at combining the most opposite elements, and were usually able, by a happy tradition inherited from our founder, to hold them suspended in a temporary harmony. Then there was Cantilupe, who had recently retired from public life, and whose name, perhaps, is already beginning to be forgotten. Of younger men we had Allison, who, though still engaged in business, was already active in his socialist propaganda. Angus Mac-Carthy, too, was there, a man whose tragic end at Saint Petersburg is still fresh in our minds. And there were others of less note; Wilson, the biologist, Professor Martin, Coryat, the poet, and one or two more who will be mentioned in their place.

After dinner, the time of year being June, and the weather unusually warm, we adjourned to the terrace for our coffee and cigars. The air was so pleasant and the prospect so beautiful, the whole weald of Sussex lying before us in the evening light, that it was suggested we should hold our meeting there rather than indoors. This was agreed. But it then transpired that Cantilupe, who was to have read the paper, had brought nothing to read. He had forgotten, or he had been too busy. At this discovery there was a general cry of protest. Cantilupe's proposition that we should forego our discussion was indignantly scouted; and he was pressed to improvise something on the lines of what he had intended to write. This, however, he steadily declined to attempt; and it seemed as though the debate would fall through, until it occurred to me to intervene in my capacity as chairman.

"Cantilupe," I said, "certainly ought to be somehow penalized. And since he declines to improvise a paper, I propose that he improvise a speech. He is accustomed to doing that; and since he has now retired from public life, this may be his last opportunity. Let him employ it, then, in doing penance. And the penance I impose is, that he should make a personal confession. That he should tell us why he has been a politician, why he has been, and is, a Tory, and why he is now retiring in the prime of life. I propose, in a word, that he should give us his point of view. That will certainly provoke Remenham, on whom I shall call next. He will provoke some one else. And so we shall all find ourselves giving our points of view, and we ought to have a very interesting evening." This suggestion was greeted, if not with enthusiasm, at least with acquiescence. Cantilupe at first objected strongly, but yielded to pressure, and on my calling formally upon him rose reluctantly from his seat. For a minute or two he stood silent, humping his shoulders and smiling through his thick beard. Then, in his slow, deliberate way, he began as follows:

"Why I went into politics? Why did I? I 'm sure I don't know. Certainly I was n't intended for it. I was intended for a country gentleman, and I hope for the rest of my life to be one; which, perhaps, it I were candid, is the real reason of my retirement. But I was pushed into politics when I was young, as a kind of family duty; and once in it 's very hard to get out again. I 'm coming out now because, among other things, there's no longer any place for me. Toryism is dead. And I, as you justly describe me, am a Tory. But you want to know why? Well, I don't know that I can tell you. Perhaps I ought to be able to. Remenham, I know, can and will give you the clearest possible account of why he is a Liberal. But then Remenham has principles; and I have only prejudices. I am a Tory because I was born one, just as another man is a Radical because he was born one. But Remenham, I really believe, is a Liberal, because he has convinced himself that he ought to be one. I admire him for it, but I am quite unable to understand him. And, for my own part, if I am to defend, or rather to explain myself, I can only do so by explaining my prejudices. And really I am glad to have the opportunity of doing so, if only because it is a satisfaction occasionally to say what one thinks; a thing which has become impossible in public life.

"The first of my prejudices is that I believe in inequality. I 'm not at all sure that that is a prejudice confined to myself — most people seem to act upon it in practice, even in America. But I not only recognize the fact, I approve the ideal of inequality. I don't want, myself, to be the equal of Darwin or of the German Emperor; and I don't see why anybody should want to be my equal. I like a society properly ordered in ranks and classes. I like my butcher or my gardener to take off his hat to me, and I like, myself, to stand bare-headed in the presence of the Queen. I don't know that I 'm better or worse than the village carpenter; but I 'm different; and I like him to recognize that fact, and to recognize it myself. In America, I am told, every one is always inform-ing you, in everything they do and say, directly or indirectly, that they are as good as you are. That is n't true, and if it were, it is n't good manners to keep saying it. I prefer a society where people have places and know them. They always do have places in any possible society; only, in a democratic society, they refuse to recognize them; and, conse-quently, social relations are much ruder, more un-pleasant and less humane than they are, or used to be, in England. That is my first prejudice; and it follows, of course, that I hate the whole democratic movement. I see no sense in pretending to make people equal politically when they 're unequal in every other respect. Do what you may, it will al-ways be a few people that will govern. And the only real result of the extension of the franchise has been to transfer political power from the landlords to

[8]

the trading classes and the wire-pullers. Well, I don't think the change is a good one. And that brings me to my second prejudice, a prejudice against trade. I don't mean, of course, that we can do without it. A country must have wealth, though I think we were a much better country when we had less than we have now. Nor do I dispute that there are to be found excellent, honourable, and capable men of business. But I believe that the pursuit of wealth tends to unfit men for the service of the state. And I sympathize with the somewhat extreme view of the ancient world that those who are engaged in trade ought to be excluded from public functions. I believe in government by gentlemen; and the word gentleman I understand in the proper, old-fashioned English sense, as a man of independent means, brought up from his boyhood in the atmosphere of public life, and destined either for the army, the navy, the Church, or Parliament. It was that kind of man that made Rome great, and that made England great in the past; and I don't believe that a country will ever be great which is governed by merchants and shopkeepers and artisans. Not because they are not, or may not be, estimable people; but because their occupations and manner of life unfit them for public service.

"Well, that is the kind of feeling—I won't call it a principle — which determined my conduct in public life. And you will remember that it seemed to be far more possible to give expression to it when first I entered politics than it is now. Even after the first Reform Act — which, in my opinion was conceived upon the wrong lines — the landed gentry still governed England; and if I could have had my way they would have continued to do so. It was n't really parliamentary reform that was wanted; it was better and more intelligent government. And such government the then ruling class was capable of supplying, as is shown by the series of measures passed in the thirties and forties, the new Poor Law and the Public Health Acts and the rest. Even the repeal of the Corn Laws shows at least how capable they were of sacrificing their own interests to the nation; though otherwise I consider that measure the greatest of their blunders. I don't profess to be a political economist, and I am ready to take it from those whose business it is to know that our wealth has been increased by

Free Trade. But no one has ever convinced me, though many people have tried, that the increase of wealth ought to be the sole object of a nation's policy. And it is surely as clear as day that the policy of Free Trade has dislocated the whole structure of our society. It has substituted a miserable city-proletariat for healthy labourers on the soil; it has transferred the great bulk of wealth from the country-gentlemen to the traders; and in so doing it has more and more transferred power from those who had the tradition of using it to those who have no tradition at all except that of accumulation. The very thing which I should have thought must be the main business of a statesman — the determination of the proper relations of classes to one another—we have handed over to the chances of competition. We have abandoned the problem in despair, instead of attempting to solve it; with the result, that our population — so it seems to me — is daily degenerating before our eyes, in physique, in morals, in taste, in everything that matters; while we console ourselves with the increasing aggregate of our wealth. Free Trade, in my opinion, was the first great betrayal by the governing class of the country and themselves, and the second was the extension of the franchise. I do not say that I would not have made any change at all in the parliamentary system that had been handed down to us. But I would never have admitted, even implicitly, that every man has a right to vote, still less that all have an equal right. For society, say what we may, is not composed of individuals but of classes; and by classes it ought to be represented. I would have enfranchised peasants, artisans, merchants, manufacturers, as such, taking as my unit the interest, not the individual, and assigning to each so much weight as would enable its influence to be felt, while preserving to the landed gentry their preponderance. That would have been difficult, no doubt, but it would have been worth doing; whereas it was, to my mind, as foolish as it was easy simply to add new batches of electors, till we shall arrive, I do not doubt, at what, in effect, is universal suffrage, without having ever admitted to ourselves that we wanted to have it.

"But what has been done is final and irremediable. Henceforth, numbers, or rather those who control numbers, will dominate England; and they will not be the men under whom hitherto she has grown great. For people like myself there is no longer a place in politics. And really, so far as I am personally concerned, I am rather glad to know it. Those who have got us into the mess must get us out of it. Probably they will do so, in their own way; but they will make, in the process, a very different England from the one I have known and understood and loved. We shall have a population of city people, better fed and housed, I hope, than they are now, clever and quick and smart, living entirely by their heads, ready to turn out in a moment for use everything they know, but knowing really very little, and not knowing it very well. There will be fewer of the kind of people in whom I take pleasure, whom I like to regard as peculiarly English, and who are the products of the countryside; fellows who grow like vegetables, and, without knowing how, put on sense as they put on flesh by an unconscious process of assimilation; who will stand for an hour at a time watching a horse or a pig, with stolid moon-faces as motionless as a pond; the sort of men that visitors from town imagine to be stupid because they take five minutes to answer a question, and then probably answer by asking another; but who have stored up in them a wealth of experience far too extensive and complicated for them ever to have taken account of it. They live by their instincts not their brains; but their instincts are the slow deposit of long years of practical dealings with nature. That is the kind of man I like. And I like to live among them in the way I do — in a traditional relation which it never occurs to them to resent, any more than it does to me to abuse it. That sort of relation you can't create; it has to grow, and to be handed down from father to son. The new men who come on to the land never manage to establish it. They bring with them the isolation which is the product of cities. They have no idea of any tie except that of wages; the notion of neighbourliness they do not understand. And that reminds me of a curious thing. People go to town for society; but I have always found that there is no real society except in the country. We may be stupid there, but we belong to a scheme of things which embodies the wisdom of generations. We meet not in drawing-

rooms, but in the hunting-field, on the county-bench, at dinners of tenants or farmers' associations. Our private business is intermixed with our public. Our occupation does not involve competition; and the daily performance of its duties we feel to be itself a kind of national service. That is an order of things which I understand and admire, as my fathers understood and admired it before me. And that is why I am a Tory; not because of any opinions I hold, but because that is my character. I stood for Toryism while it meant something; and now that it means nothing, though I stand for it no longer, still I can't help *being* it. The England that is will last my time; the England that is to be does not interest me; and it is as well that I should have nothing to do with directing it.

"I don't know whether that is a sufficient account of the question I was told to answer; but it's the best I can make, and I think it ought to be sufficient. I always imagine myself saying to God, if He asks me to give an account of myself: 'Here I am, as you made me. You can take me or leave me. If I had to live again I would live just so. And if you want me to live differently, you must make me different.' I have championed a losing cause, and I am sorry it has lost. But I do not break my heart about it. I can still live for the rest of my days the life I respect and enjoy. And I am content to leave the nation in the hands of Remenham, who, as I see, is all impatience to reply to my heresies."

REMENHAM in fact was fidgetting in his chair as though he found it hard to keep his seat; and I should have felt bound in pity to call upon him next, even if I had not already determined to do so. He rose with alacrity; and it was impossible not to be struck by the contrast he presented to Cantilupe. His elastic upright figure, his firm chin, the exuberance of his gestures, the clear ring of his voice, expressed admirably the intellectual and nervous force which he possessed in a higher degree than any man I have ever come across. He began without hesitation, and spoke throughout with the trained and facile eloquence of which he was master. "I shall, I am sure, be believed," he said, "when I emphatically assert that nothing could be more distressing to me than the notion — if I should be driven to accept it — that the liberal measures on which, in my opinion, the prosperity and the true welfare of the country depends should have, as one of their incidental concomitants, the withdrawal from public life of such men as our friend who has just sat down. We need all the intellectual and moral resources of the country; and among them I count as not the least valuable and fruitful the stock of our ancient country gentlemen. I regretted the retirement of Lord Cantilupe on public as well as on personal grounds; and my regret is only tempered, not altogether removed, when I see how well, how honourably and how happily he is employing his well-deserved leisure. But I am glad to know that we have still, and to believe that we shall continue to have, in the great Council of the nation, men of his distinguished type and tradition to form one, and that not the least important, of the balances and counter-checks in the great and complicated engine of state.

" When, however, he claims — or perhaps I should rather say desires — for the distinguished order of which he is a member, an actual and permanent preponderance in the state, there, I confess, I must part company with him. Nay, I cannot even accept the theory, to which he gave expression, of a fixed and stable representation of interests. It is indeed true that society, by the mysterious dispensation of the Divine Being, is wonderfully compounded of the most diverse elements and classes, corresponding to the various needs and requirements of human life. And it is an ancient theory, supported by the authority of great names, by Plato, my revered master, the poet-philosopher, by Aristotle, the founder of political science, that the problem of a statesman is so to adjust these otherwise discordant elements as to form once for all in the body-politic a perfect, a final and immutable harmony. There is, according to this view, one simple chord and one only, which the great organ of society is adapted to play; and the business of the legislator is merely to tune the instrument so that it shall play it correctly. Thus, if Plato could have had his way, his great common chord, his harmony of producers, soldiers and philosophers, would still have been droning monotonously down the ages, wherever men were assembled to dwell together. Doubtless the concord he conceived was beautiful. But the dissonances he

would have silenced, but which, with ever-aug-
menting force, peal and crash, from his day to
ours, through the echoing vault of time, embody,
as I am apt to think, a harmony more august than
any which even he was able to imagine, and in
their intricate succession weave the plan of a
world-symphony too high to be apprehended save
in part by our grosser sense, but perceived with
delight by the pure intelligence of immortal spirits.
It is indeed the fundamental defect of all imaginary polities — and how much more of such as fos-
silize, without even idealizing, the actual! — that
even though they be perfect, their perfection is relative only to a single set of conditions; and that
could they perpetuate themselves they would also
perpetuate these, which should have been but brief
and transitory phases in the history of the race.
Had it been possible for Plato to establish over the
habitable globe his golden chain of philosophic
cities, he would have rivetted upon the world for
ever the institutions of slavery and caste, would
have sealed at the source the springs of science and
invention, and imprisoned in perennial impotence
that mighty genius of empire which alone has been

able to co-ordinate to a common and beneficent end the stubborn and rebellious members of this growing creature Man. And if the imagination of a Plato, permitted to work its will, would thus have sterilized the germs of progress, what shall we say of such men as ourselves imposing on the fecundity of nature the limits and rules of our imperfect mensuration! Rather should we, in humility, submit ourselves to her guidance, and so adapt our institutions that they shall hamper as little as may be the movements and forces operating within them. For it is by conflict, as we have now learnt, that the higher emerges from the lower, and nature herself, it would almost seem, does not direct but looks on, as her world emerges in painful toil from chaos. We do not find her with precipitate zeal intervening to arrest at a given point the ferment of creation; stretching her hand when she sees the gleam of the halcyon or the rose to bid the process cease that would destroy them; and sacrificing to the completeness of those lower forms the nobler imperfection of man and of what may lie beyond him. She looks always to the end; and so in our statesmanship should we, striving to express, not to limit, by our institutions the forces with which we have to deal. Our polity should grow, like a skin, upon the living tissue of society. For who are we that we should say to this man or that, go plough, keep shop, or govern the state? That we should say to the merchant, 'thus much power shall be yours,' and to the farmer 'thus much yours?' No! rather let us say to each and to all, Take the place you can, enjoy the authority you can win! Let our constitution express the balance of forces in our society, and as they change let the disposition of power change with them! That is the creed of liberalism, supported by nature herself, and sanctioned, I would add with reverence, by the Almighty Power, in the disposition and order of his stupendous creation.

"But it is not a creed that levels, nor one that destroys. None can have more regard than I — not Cantilupe himself — for our ancient crown, our hereditary aristocracy. These, while they deserve it — and long may they do so! — will retain their honoured place in the hearts and affections of the people. Only, alongside of them, I would make room for all elements and interests that may come into being in the natural course of the play of social forces. But these will be far too numerous, far too inextricably interwoven, too rapidly changing in relative weight and importance, for the intelligence of man to attempt, by any artificial scheme, to balance and adjust their conflicting claims. Open to all men equally, within the limits of prudence, the avenue to political influence, and let them use, as they can and will, in combined or isolated action, the opportunities thus liberally bestowed. That is the key-note of the policy which I have consistently adopted from my entrance into public life, and which I am prepared to prosecute to the end, though that end should be the universal suffrage so dreaded by the last speaker. He tells me it is a policy of reckless abandonment. But abandonment to what? Abandonment to the people! And the question is, do we trust the people? I do; he does not! There, I venture to think, is the real difference between us.

"Yes, I am not ashamed to say it, I trust the People! What should I trust, if I could not trust them? What else is a nation but an assemblage of the talents, the capacities, the virtues of the citizens of whom it is composed? To utilize those talents, to evoke those capacities, to offer scope and opportunity to those virtues, must be the end and purpose of every great and generous policy; and to that end, up to the measure of my powers, I have striven to minister, not rashly, I hope, nor with impatience, but in the spirit of a sober and assured faith.

'Such is my conception of liberalism. But if liberalism has its mission at home, not less important are its principles in the region of international relations. I will not now embark on the troubled sea of foreign policy. But on one point I will touch, since it was raised by the last speaker, and that is the question of our foreign trade. In no department of human activity, I will venture to say, are the intentions of the Almighty more plainly indicated, than in this of the interchange of the products of labour. To each part of the habitable globe have been assigned its special gifts for the use and delectation of Man; to every nation its peculiar skill, its appropriate opportunities. As the world was created for labour, so it was created for exchange. Across the ocean, bridged at last by the indomitable perti-

nacity of art, the granaries of the new world call, in
their inexhaustible fecundity, for the iron and
steel, the implements and engines of the old. The
shepherd-kings of the limitless plains of Australia,
the Indian ryot, the now happily emancipated ne-
gro of Georgia and Carolina, feed and are fed by
the factories and looms of Manchester and Brad-
ford. Pall-Mall is made glad with the produce of
the vineyards of France and Spain; and the Italian
peasant goes clad in the labours of the Leicester
artisan. The golden chain revolves, the silver
buckets rise and fall; and one to the other passes
on, as it fills and overflows, the stream that pours
from Nature's cornucopia! Such is the law or-
dained by the Power that presides over the des-
tinies of the world; and not all the interferences of
man with His beneficent purposes can avail altogether to check and frustrate their happy operation. Yet have the blind cupidity, the ignorant ap-
prehensions of national zeal dislocated, so far as
was possible, the wheels and cogs of the great
machine, hampered its working and limited its
uses. And if there be anything of which this great
nation may justly boast, it is that she has been the

first to tear down the barriers and dams of a perverted ingenuity, and to admit in unrestricted plenitude to every channel of her verdant meadows the limpid and fertilizing stream of trade.

" Verily she has had her reward! Search the records of history, and you will seek in vain for a prosperity so immense, so continuous, so progressive, as that which has blessed this country in the last half-century of her annals. This access of wealth was admitted indeed by the speaker who preceded me. But he complained that we had taken no account of the changes which the new system was introducing into the character and occupations of the people. It is true; and he would be a rash man who should venture to forecast and to determine the remoter results of such a policy; or should shrink from the consequences of liberty on the ground that he cannot anticipate their character. Which of us would have the courage, even if he had the power, to impose upon a nation for all time the form of its economic life, the type of its character, the direction of its enterprise ? The possibilities that lie in the womb of Nature are greater than we can gauge;

we can but facilitate their birth, we may not prescribe their anatomy. The evils of the day call for the remedies of the day; but none can anticipate with advantage the necessities of the future. And meantime what cause is there for misgiving? I confess that I see none. The policy of freedom has been justified, I contend, by its results. And so confident am I of this, that the time, I believe, is not far distant, when other countries will awake at last to their own true interests and emulate, not more to their advantage than to ours, our fiscal legislation. I see the time approaching when the nations of the world, laying aside their political animosities, will be knitted together in the peaceful rivalry of trade; when those barriers of nationality which belong to the infancy of the race will melt and dissolve in the sunshine of science and art; when the roar of the cannon will yield to the softer murmur of the loom, and the apron of the artisan, the blouse of the peasant be more honourable than the scarlet of the soldier; when the cosmopolitan armies of trade will replace the militia of death; when that which God has joined together will no longer be sundered by the ignorance, the folly, the wickedness of man; when the labour and the invention of one will become the heritage of all; and the peoples of the earth meet no longer on the field of battle, but by their chosen delegates, as in the vision of our greatest poet, in the 'Parliament of Man, the Federation of the World.'"

WITH this peroration Remenham resumed his seat. He had spoken, as indeed was his habit, rather as if he were addressing a public meeting than a company of friends. But at least he had set the ball rolling. To many of those present, as I well knew, his speech and his manner must have been eminently provocative; and naturally to none more than to Mendoza. I had, therefore, no hesitation in signalling out the Conservative chief to give us the opposite point of view. He responded with deliberation, lifting from his chest his sinister Jewish face, and slowly unfolding his long body, while a malicious smile played about his mouth.

"One," he began, "who has not the privilege of immediate access to the counsels of the Divine Being cannot but feel himself at a disadvantage in following a man so favoured as my distinguished friend. The disadvantage, however, is one to which I have had, perforce, to grow accustomed during long years of parliamentary strife. I have resigned myself to creeping where he soars, to guessing where he prophesies. But there is compensation everywhere. And, perhaps, there are certain points which may be revealed to babes and sucklings, while they are concealed from beings more august. The worm, I suppose, must be aware of excrescences and roughnesses of the soil which escape the more comprehensive vision of the eagle; and to the worm, at least, these are of more importance than mountain ranges and oceans which he will never reach. It is from that humble point of view that I shall offer a few remarks supplementary to, perhaps even critical of, the eloquent apostrophe we have been permitted to enjoy.

"The key-note of my friend's address was liberty. There is no British heart which does not beat higher at the sound of that word. But while I listened to his impassioned plea, I could not help wondering why he did not propose to dispense to us in even larger and more liberal measure the supreme and precious gift of freedom. True, he has done much to remove the barriers that separated nation from nation, and man from man. But how much remains to be accomplished before we can be truly said to have brought ourselves into line with Nature! Consider, for example, the policeman! Has my friend ever reflected on all that is implied in that solemn figure; on all that it symbolizes of interference with the purposes of a beneficent Creator? The policeman is a permanent public defiance of Nature. Through him the weak rule the strong, the few the many, the intelligent the fools. Through him survive those whom the struggle for existence should have eliminated. He substitutes the unfit for the fit. He dislocates the economy of the universe. Under his shelter take root and thrive all monstrous and parasitic growths. Marriage clings to his skirts, property nestles in his bosom. And while these flourish, where is liberty? The law of Nature we all know:

> ' *The good old rule, the ancient plan*
> *That he should take who has the power,*
> *And he should keep who can!* '

"But this, by the witchcraft of property, we have set aside. Our walls of brick and stone we

[29]

have manned with invisible guards. We have thronged with fiery faces and arms the fences of our gardens and parks. The plate-glass of our windows we have made more impenetrable than adamant. To our very infants we have given the strength of giants. Babies surfeit, while strong men starve; and the foetus in the womb stretches out unformed hands to annex a principality. Is this liberty? Is this Nature? No! It is a Merlin's prison! Yet, monstrous, it subsists! Has our friend, then, no power to dissolve the charm? Or, can it be that he has not the will?

"Again, can we be said to be free, can we be said to be in harmony with Nature, while we endure the bonds of matrimony? While we fetter the happy promiscuity of instinct, and subject our roving fancy to the dominion of 'one unchanging wife?' Here, indeed, I frankly admit, Nature has her revenges; and an actual polygamy flourishes even under the aegis of our law. But the law exists; it is the warp on which, by the woof of property, we fashion that Nessus-shirt, the Family, in which, we have swathed the giant energies of mankind. But while that shirt clings close to every limb, what avails it, in the name of liberty, to snap, here and there, a button or a lace? A more heroic work is required of the great protagonist, if, indeed, he will follow his mistress to the end. He shakes his head. What! Is his service, then, but half-hearted after all? Or, can it be, that behind the mask of the goddess he begins to divine the teeth and claws of the brute? But if nature be no goddess, how can we accept her as sponsor for liberty? And if liberty be taken on its own merits how is it to be distinguished from anarchy? How, but by the due admixture of coercion? And, that admitted, must we not descend from the mountain top of prophecy to the dreary plains of political compromise?"

Up to this point Mendoza had preserved that tone of elaborate irony which, it will be remembered, was so disconcerting to English audiences, and stood so much in the way of his popularity. But now his manner changed. Becoming more serious, and I fear I must add, more dull than I had ever heard him before, he gave us what I suppose to be the most intimate exposition he had ever permitted himself to offer of the Conservative point of view as he understood it.

"These," he resumed, "are questions which I must leave my friend to answer for himself. The ground is too high for me. I have no skill in the flights of speculation. I take no pleasure in the enunciation of principles. To my restricted vision, placed as I am upon the earth, isolated facts obtrude themselves with a capricious particularity which defies my powers of generalization. And that, perhaps, is the reason why I attached myself to the party to which I have the honour to belong. For it is, I think, the party which sees things as they are; as they are, that is, to mere human vision. Remenham, in his haste, has called us the party of reaction. I would rather say, we are the party of realism. We have in view, not Man, but Englishmen; not ideal polities, but the British Constitution; not Political Economy, but the actual course of our trade. Through this great forest of fact, this tangle of old and new, these secular oaks, sturdy shrubs, beautiful parasitic creepers, we move with a prudent diffidence, following the old tracks, endeavouring to keep them open, but hesitating to cut new routes till we are clear as to the goal for which we are asked to sacrifice our finest timber.

Fundamental changes we regard as exceptional and pathological. Yet, being bound by no theories, when we are convinced of their necessity, we inaugurate them boldly and carry them through to the end. And thus it is that having decided that the time had come to call the people to the councils of the nation, we struck boldly and once for all by a measure which I will never admit — and here I regret that Cantilupe is not with me — which I will never admit to be at variance with the best and soundest traditions of conservatism.

"But such measures are exceptional, and we hope they will be final. We take no delight in tinkering the constitution. The mechanism of government we recognize to be only a means; the test of the statesman is his power to govern. And remaining, as we do, inaccessible to that gospel of liberty of which our opponents have had a special revelation, we find in the existing state of England much that appears to us to need control. We are unable to share the optimism which animates Remenham and his friends as to the direction and effects of the new forces of industry. Above the whirr of the spindle and the shaft we hear the cry of the poor.

Behind our flourishing warehouses and shops we see the hovels of the artisan. We watch along our highroads the long procession of labourers deserting their ancestral villages for the cities; we trace them to the slum and the sweater's den; we follow them to the poorhouse and the prison; we see them disappear engulfed in the abyss, while others press at their heels to take their place and share their destiny. And in face of all this we do not think it to be our duty to fold our arms and invoke the principle of liberty. We feel that we owe it to the nation to preserve intact its human heritage, the only source of its greatness and its wealth; and we are prepared, with such wisdom as we have, to legislate to that end, undeterred by the fear of incurring the charge of socialism.

"But while we thus concern ourselves with the condition of these islands, we have not forgotten that we have relations to the world outside. If, indeed, we could share the views to which Remenham has given such eloquent expression, this is a matter which would give us little anxiety. He beholds, as in a vision, the era of peace and good-will ushered in by the genius of commerce. By a mysterious dispensation of Providence he sees cupidity and competition furthering the ends of charity and peace. But here once more I am unable to follow his audacious flight. Confined to the sphere of observation, I cannot but note that in the long and sanguinary course of history there has been no cause so fruitful of war as the rivalries of trade. Our own annals at every point are eloquent of this truth; nor do I see anything in the conditions of the modern world that should limit its application. We have been told that all nations will adopt our fiscal policy. Why should they, unless it is to their interest? We adopted it because we thought it was to ours; and we shall abandon it if we ever change our opinion. And when I say 'interest' I would not be understood to mean economic interest in the narrower sense. A nation, like an individual, I conceive, has a personality to maintain. It must be its object not to accumulate wealth at all costs, but to develope and maintain capacity, to be powerful, energetic, many-sided, and above all independent. Whether the policy we have adopted will continue to guarantee this result, I am not prophet enough to venture to affirm. But if it does not, I cannot doubt that we shall be driven to revise it. Nor can I believe that other nations, not even our own colonies, will follow us in our present policy, if to do so would be to jeopardy their rising industries and unduly to narrow the scope of their economic energies. I do not, then, I confess, look forward with enthusiasm or with hope to the Crystal-Palace millennium that inspired the eloquence of Remenham. I see the future pregnant with wars and rumours of wars. And in particular I see this nation, by virtue of its wealth, its power, its unparalleled success, the target for the envy, the hatred, the cupidity of all the peoples of Europe. I see them looking abroad for outlets for their expanding population, only to find every corner of the habitable globe preoccupied by the English race and overshadowed by the English flag. But from this, which is our main danger, I conjure my main hope for the future. England is more than England. She has grown in her sleep. She has stretched over every continent huge embryo limbs which wait only for the beat of her heart, the motion of her spirit, to assume their form and function as members of one great body of empire. The spirit, I think, begins to stir, the blood to circulate. Our colonies, I believe, are not destined to drop from us like ripe fruit; our dependencies will not fall to other masters. The nation sooner or later will wake to its imperial mission. The hearts of Englishmen beyond the seas will beat in unison with ours. And the federation I foresee is not the federation of Mankind, but that of the British race throughout the world."

He paused, and in the stillness that followed we became aware of the gathering dusk. The first stars were appearing, and the young moon was low in the west. From the shadow below we heard the murmur of a fountain, and the call of a nightingale sounded in the wood. Something in the time and the place must have worked on Mendoza's mood; for when he resumed it was in a different key.

"Such," he began, "is my vision, if I permit myself to dream. But who shall say whether it is more than a dream? There is something in the air to-night which compels candour. And if I am to tell my inmost thought, I must confess on what a flood of nescience we, who seem to direct the affairs of nations, are borne along together with those whom we appear to control. We are permitted, like children, to lay our hands upon the reins; but it is a dark and unknown genius who drives. We are his creatures; and it is his ends, not ours, that are furthered by our contests, our efforts, our ideals. In the arena Remenham and I must play our part, combat bravely, and be ready to die when the crowd turn down their thumbs. But here in a moment of withdrawal, I at least cannot fail to recognize behind the issues that divide us the tie of a common destiny. We shall pass and a new generation will succeed us; a generation to whom our ideals will be irrelevant, our catch-words empty, our controversies unintelligible.

*Hi motus animorum atque haec certamina tanta
Pulveris exigui jactu compressa quiescunt.'*

"The dust of oblivion will bury our debates. Something we shall have achieved, but not what we intended. My dream may, perhaps, be furthered by Remenham, and his by me, or, it may be, neither his nor mine by either. The Providence whose purposes he so readily divines is dark to me. And perhaps, for that reason, I am able to regard

him with more charity than he has always been willing, I suspect, to extend to me. This, at any rate,
is the moment of truce. The great arena is empty,
the silent benches vanish into the night. Under the
glimmer of the moon figures more than mortal
haunt the scene of our ephemeral contests. It is
they which stand behind us and deal the blows
which seem to be ours. When we are laid in the
dust they will animate other combatants; when
our names are forgotten they will blazon others in
perishable gold. Why, then, should we strive and
cry, even now in the twilight hour? The same
sky encompasses us, the same stars are above us.
What are my opinions, what are Remenham's?
Froth on the surface! The current bears all alike
along to the destined end. For a moment let us
meet and feel its silent, irresistible force; and in
this moment reach across the table the hand of
peace."

With that he stretched his hand to Remenham,
with a kind of pathos of appeal that the other,
though I think he did not altogether like it, could
hardly refuse to entertain. It was theatrical, it was
un-English, but somehow, it was successful. And

the whole episode, the closing words and the incomparable gesture, left me with a sense as though a curtain had been drawn upon a phase of our history. Mendoza, somehow, had shut out Remenham, even more than himself, from the field on which the issues of the future were to be fought. And it was this feeling that led me, really a little against my inclination, to select as the next speaker the man who of all who made up our company, in opinions, was the most opposed to Remenham, and in temperament to Mendoza. My choice was Allison, more famous now than he was then, but known even at that time as an unsparing critic of both parties. He responded readily enough; and as he began a spell seemed to snap. The night and the hour were forgotten, and we were back on the dusty field of controversy.

"THIS is all very touching," he began, "but Mendoza is shaking hands with the wrong person. He's much nearer to me than he is to Remenham, and I don't at all despair of converting him. For he does at least understand that the character of every society depends upon its law of property; and he even seems to have a suspicion that the law, as we have it, is not what you would call absolute perfection. It 's true that he shows no particular inclination to alter it. But that may come; and I 'm not without hope of seeing, before I die, a Tory-Socialist party. Remenham's is a different case, and I fear there 's nothing to be made of him. He does, I believe, really think that in some extraordinary way the law of property, like the Anglican Church, is one of the dispensations of Providence; and that if he removes all other restrictions, leaving that, he will have what he calls a natural society. But Nature, as Mendoza has pointed out, is anarchy. Civilization means restriction; and so does socialism. So far from being anarchy, it is the very antithesis of it. Anarchy is the goal of liberalism, if liberalism could ever be persuaded to be logical. So the scarecrow of anarchy, at least, need not frighten away any would-be convert to socialism. There remains, it is true, the other scarecrow, revolution; and that, I admit, has more life in it. Socialism *is* revolutionary; but so is liberalism, or was, while it was anything. Revolution does not imply violence. On the contrary, violence is the abortion of revolution. Do

I, for instance, look like a Marat or a Danton? I ask you, candidly!"

He certainly did not. On the contrary, with his short squat figure, pointed beard and spectacles, he presented a curious blend of the middle-class Englishman and the German savant. There was a burst of laughter at his question, in which he joined himself. But when he resumed it was in a more serious tone and somewhat in the manner of a lecturer. It was indeed, at that time, very largely by lectures that he carried on his propaganda.

"No," he said, "socialism may roar; but, in England at any rate, it roars as gently as any sucking-dove. Revolution I admit is the goal; but the process is substitution. We propose to transform society almost without any one knowing it; to work from the foundation upwards without unduly disturbing the superstructure. By a mere adjustment of rates and taxes we shall redistribute property; by an extension of the powers of local bodies we shall nationalize industry. But in all this there need be no shock, no abrupt transition. On the contrary, it is essential to our scheme that there should not be. We are men of science and we real-

[42]

ize that the whole structure of society rests upon habit. With the new organization must therefore grow the new habit that is to support it. To precipitate organic change is merely to court reaction. That is the lesson of all revolution; and it is one which English socialists, at any rate, have learnt. We think, moreover, that capitalist society is, by its own momentum, travelling towards the goal which we desire. Every consolidation of business upon a grand scale implies the development of precisely those talents of organization without which the socialistic state could not come into being or maintain itself; while at the same time the substitution of monopoly for competition removes the only check upon the power of capital to exploit society, and brings home to every citizen in his tenderest point — his pocket — the necessity for that public control from which he might otherwise be inclined to shrink. Capitalist society is thus preparing its own euthanasia; and we socialists ought to be regarded not as assassins of the old order, but as midwives to deliver it of the child with which it is in travail.

"That child will be a society not of liberty but of

regulation. It is here that we join issue not only with doctrinaire liberals, but with that large body of ordinary common-sense Englishmen who feel a general and instinctive distrust of all state interference. That distrust, I would point out, is really an anachronism. It dates from a time when the state was at once incompetent and unpopular, from the days of monarchic or aristocratic government carried on frankly in the interests of particular classes or persons. But the democratic revolution and the introduction of bureaucracy has swept all that away; and governments in every civilized country are now moving towards the ideal of an expert administration controlled by an alert and intelligent public opinion. Much, it is true, has yet to be done before that ideal will be realized. In some countries, notably in the United States, the necessity of the expert has hardly made itself felt. In others, such as Germany, popular control is very inadequately provided for. But the tendency is clear; and nowhere clearer than in this country. Here at any rate we may hopefully look forward to a continual extension both of the activity and of the intelligence of public officials; while at the same time, by an appropriate development of the representative machinery, we may guard ourselves against the danger of an irresponsible bureaucracy. The problem of reconciling administrative efficiency with popular control is no doubt a difficult one; but I feel confident that it can be solved. This perhaps is hardly the place to develop my favourite idea of the professional representative; but I may be permitted to refer to it in passing. By a professional representative I mean one trained in a scientific and systematic way to elicit the real opinion of his constituents, and to embody it in practicable proposals. He will have to study what they really want, not what they think they want, and to discover for himself in what way it can be obtained. Such men need not be elected; indeed I am inclined to think that the plan of popular election has had its day. The essential is that they should be selected by some test of efficiency, such as examination or previous record, and that they should keep themselves in constant touch with their constituents. But I must not dwell upon details. My main object is to show that when government is in the hands of expert administrators, controlled by expert representatives, there need be no anxiety felt in extending indefinitely the sphere of the state.

"This extension will of course be primarily economic, for, as is now generally recognized, the whole character of a society depends upon its economic organization. Revolution, if it is to be profound, must begin with the organization of industry; but it does not follow that it will end there. It is a libel on the socialist ideal to call it materialistic, to say that it is indifferent or hostile to the higher activities. No one, to begin with, is more conscious than a true socialist of the importance of science. Not only is the sociology on which his position is based a branch of science; but it is a fundamental part of his creed that the progress of man depends upon his mastery of Nature, and that for acquiring that mastery science is his only weapon. Again, it is absurd to accuse us of indifference to ethics. Our standards, indeed, may not be the same as those of bourgeois society; if they were, that would be their condemnation; for a new economic régime necessarily postulates a new ethic. But every régime requires and produces its appropriate standards; and the socialist régime will be no exception. Our feeling upon that subject is simply that we need not trouble about the ethic because it will follow of itself upon the economic revolution. For, as we read history, the economic factor determines all the others. 'Man ist was er isst,' as the German said; and morals, art, religion, all the so-called 'ideal activities,' are just allotropic forms of bread and meat. They will come by themselves if they are wanted; and in the socialist state they will be better not worse provided for than under the present competitive system. For here again the principle of the expert will come in. It will be the business of the state, if it determines that such activities ought to be encouraged, to devise a machinery for selecting and educating men of genius, in proportion to the demand, and assigning to them their appropriate sphere of activity and their sufficient wage. This will apply, I conceive, equally to the ministers of religion as to the professors of the various branches of art. Nor would I suggest that the socialist community should establish any one form of religion, seeing that we are not in a position to determine scientifically which, or whether any, are true. I would give encourage-

ment to all and several, of course under the necessary restrictions, in the hope that, in course of time,
by a process of natural selection, that one will survive which is the best adapted to the new environment. But meantime the advantage of the new over
the old organization is apparent. We shall hear no
more of genius starving in a garret; of ill-paid or
over-paid ministers of the gospel; of privileged and
unprivileged sects. All will be orderly, regular, and
secure, as it should be in a civilized state; and for
the first time in history society will be in a position to extract the maximum of good from those
strange and irregular human organizations whose
subsistence hitherto has been so precarious and
whose output so capricious and uncertain. A socialist state, if I may say so, will pigeon-hole religion, literature and art; and if these are really
normal and fruitful functions they cannot fail,
like other functions, to profit by such treatment.

"I have thus indicated in outline the main features of the socialist scheme — an economic revolution accomplished by a gradual and peaceful
transition and issuing in a system of collectivism so

complete as to include all the human activities that
are really valuable. But what I should find it hard
to convey, except to an audience prepared by years
of study, is the enthusiasm or rather the grounds
for the enthusiasm, that animates us. Whereas all
other political parties are groping in the dark, rely-
ing upon partial and outworn formulæ, in which
even they themselves have ceased to believe, we
alone advance in the broad daylight, along a road
whose course we clearly trace backward and forward, towards a goal distinctly seen on the horizon.
History and analysis are our guides; history for
the first time comprehended, analysis for the first
time scientifically applied. Unlike all the revolu-
tionists of the past, we derive our inspiration not
from our own intuitions or ideals, but from the as-
certained course of the world. We co-operate with
the universe; and hence at once our confidence and
our patience. We can afford to wait because the
force of events is bearing us on of its own accord to
the end we desire. Even if we rest on our oars, none
the less we are drifting onwards; or if we are
checked for a moment the eddy in which we are
caught is merely local. Alone among all politicians

we have faith; but our faith is built upon science, and it is therefore a faith which will endure."

WITH that Allison concluded; and almost before he had done MacCarthy, without waiting my summons, had leapt to his feet and burst into an impassioned harangue. With flashing eyes and passionate gestures he delivered himself as follows, his Irish accent contrasting pleasantly with that of the last speaker.

"May God forgive me," he cried, "that ever I have called myself a socialist, if this is what socialism means! But it does not! I will rescue the word! I will reclaim it for its ancient nobler sense — socialism the dream of the world, the light of the grail on the marsh, the mystic city of Sarras, the vale of Avalon! Socialism the soul of liberty, the bond of brotherhood, the seal of equality! Who is he that with sacrilegious hands would seize our Ariel and prison him in that tree of iniquity the State? Day is not farther from night, nor Good from Evil, than the socialism of the Revolution from this of the desk and the stool, from this enemy wearing our uniform and flaunting our coat of arms. For nigh upon a century we have fought for liberty; and now they would make us gaolers to bind our own souls. 1789, 1830, 1848 — are these dates branded upon our hearts, only to stamp us as patient sheep in the flock of bureaucracy? No! They are the symbols of the spirit; and those whom they set apart, outcasts from the kingdoms of this world and citizens of the kingdom of God, wherever they wander are living flames to consume institutions and laws, and to light in the hearts of men the fires of pity and wrath and love. Our city is not built with blue books, nor cemented with office dust; nor is it bonds of red-tape that make and keep it one. No! it is the attraction, uncompelled, of spirits made free; the shadowing into outward form of the eternal joy of the soul!"

He paused and seemed to collect himself; and then in a quieter tone: "Socialism," he proceeded, "is one with anarchy! I know the terrors of that word; but they are the terrors of an evil conscience; for it is only an order founded on iniquity that dreads disorder. Why do you fear for your property and lives, you who fear anarchy? It is because you have stolen the one and misdevoted the other; because you have created by your laws the man you call the criminal; because you have bred hunger, and hunger has bred rage. For this I do not blame you, any more than I blame myself. You are yourselves victims of the system you maintain, and your enemy, no less than mine, if you knew it, is government. For government means compulsion, exclusion, distinction, separation; while anarchy is freedom, union and love. Government is based on egotism and fear, anarchy on fraternity. It is because we divide ourselves into nations that we endure the oppression of armaments; because we isolate ourselves as individuals that we invoke the protection of laws. If I did not take what my brother needs I should not fear that he would take it from me; if I did not shut myself off from his want, I should not deem it less urgent than my own. All governing persons are persons set apart. And therefore it is that whether they will or no they are oppressors, or, at best, obstructors. Shut off from the breath of popular instinct, which is the breath of life, they cannot feel, and therefore cannot think, rightly. And, in any case, how could they understand, even with the best will in the world, the multifarious interests they are expected to control? A man knows nothing but what he practises; and in every branch of work only those are fitted to direct who are themselves the workers. Intellectually, as well as morally, government is eternally bankrupt; and what is called representative government is no better than any other, for the governors are equally removed in sympathy and knowledge from the governed. Nay, experience shows, if we would but admit it, that under no system have the rulers been more incompetent and corrupt than under this which we call democratic. Is not the very word 'politician' everywhere a term of reproach? Is not a government-office everywhere synonymous with incapacity and sloth? What a miserable position is that of a member of Parliament, compelled to give his vote on innumerable questions of which he does not understand the rudiments, and giving it at the dictation of party chiefs who themselves are controlled by the blind and brainless mechanism of the caucus! The people are the slaves of their representatives, the representatives of their chiefs, and the chiefs of a conscienceless machine! And that is the last word of governmental science! Oh, divine spirit of man, in what chains have you bound yourself, and call it liberty, and clap your hands!

"And then comes one and says, 'because you are free, tie yourself tighter and tighter in your own bonds!' Are these hands not yours that fasten the knots? Why then do you fear? Here is a limb free; fasten it quick! Your head still turns; come, fix it in a vice! Now you are fast! Now you cannot move! How beautiful, how orderly, how secure! And this, and this is socialism! And it was to accomplish this that France opened the sluices that have deluged the earth with blood! What! we have broken the bonds of iron to bind ourselves in tape! We have discrowned Napoleon to crown . . . to crown. . . ."

He looked across at Allison, and suddenly pulled himself up. Then, attempting the tone of exposition, "There is only one way out of it," he resumed, "the extension of free co-operation in every department of activity, including those which at present are regulated by the State. You will say that this is impracticable; but why? Already, in all that you most care about, that is the method you actually adopt. The activities of men that are freest in the society in which we live are those of art and science and amusement. And all these are, I will not say regulated by, but expressed in, voluntary organizations, clubs, academies, societies, what you will. The Royal Society and the British Association Club are types of the right way of organizing; and it is a way that should and must be applied throughout the whole structure. Every trade and business should be conducted by a society voluntarily formed of all those who choose to engage in it, electing and removing their own officials, determining their own policy, and co-operating by free arrangement with other similar bodies. A complex interweaving of such associations, with order everywhere, compulsion nowhere, is the form of society to which I look forward, and which I see already growing up within the hard skin of the older organisms. Rules there will be but not laws, rules gladly obeyed because they will have been freely adopted, and because there will be no compulsion upon any one to remain within the brotherhood that approves and maintains them. Anarchy is not the absence of order, it is absence of force; it is the free outflowing of the spirit into the forms in which it delights; and in such forms alone, as they grow and change, can it find an expression which is not also a bondage. You will say this is chimerical. But look at history! Consider the great achievements of the Middle Age! Were they not the result of just such a movement as I describe? It was men voluntarily associating in communes and grouping themselves in guilds that built the towers and churches and adorned them with the glories of art that dazzles us still in Italy and France. The history of the growth of the state, of public authority and compulsion, is the history of the decline from Florence and Nuremberg to London and New York. As the power of the state grows the energy of the spirit dwindles; and if ever Allison's ideal should be realized, if ever the activity of the state should extend through and through to every department of life, the universal ease and comfort which may thus be disseminated throughout society will have been purchased dearly at the price of the soul. The denizens of that city will be fed, housed and clothed to perfection; only — and it is a serious drawback — only they will be dead.

" Oh!" he broke out, " if I could but get you to see that this whole order under which you live is artificial and unnecessary! But we are befogged by the systems we impose upon our imagination and call science. We have been taught to regard history as a necessary process, until we come to think it must also be a good one; that all that has ever happened ought to have happened just so and no otherwise. And thus we justify everything past and present, however palpably in contradiction with our own intuitions. But these are mere figments of the brain. History, for the most part, believe me, is one gigantic error and crime. It ought to have been other than it was; and we ought to be other than we are. There is no natural and inevitable evolution towards good; no co-operating with the universe, other than by connivance at its crimes. That little house the brain builds to shelter its own weakness must be torn down if we would face the truth and pursue the good. Then we shall see amid what blinding storms of wind and rain, what darkness of elements hostile or indifferent, our road lies across the mountains towards the city of our desire. Then and then only shall we understand the spirit of revolution. That there are things so bad that they can only be burnt up by fire; that there are obstructions so immense that they can only be exploded by dynamite; that the work of destruction is a necessary preliminary to the work of creation, for it is the destruction of the prison walls wherein the spirit is confined; and that in that work the spirit itself is the only agent, unhelped by powers of nature or powers of a world beyond — that is the creed — no, I will not say the creed, that is the insight and vision by which we of the Revolution live. By that I believe we shall triumph. But whether we triumph or no, our life itself is a victory, for it is a life lived in the spirit. To shatter material bonds that we may bind the closer the bonds of the soul, to slough dead husks that we may liberate living forms, to abolish institutions that we may evoke energies, to put off the material and put on the spiritual body, that, whether we fight with the tongue or the sword, is the inspiration of our movement, that, and that only, is the true and inner meaning of anarchy.

" Anarchy is identified with violence; and I will not be so hypocritical and base as to deny that violence must be one of our means of action. Force is the midwife of society; and never has radical change been accomplished without it. What came by the sword by the sword must be destroyed; and only through violence can violence come to an end. Nay, I will go further and confess, since here if anywhere we are candid, that it is the way of violence to which I feel called myself, and that I shall die as I have lived, an active revolutionary. But because force is a way, is a necessary way, is my way, I do not imagine that there is no other. Were it not idle to wish, I could rather wish that I were a poet or a saint, to serve the same Lord by the gentler weapons of the spirit. There are anarchists who never made a speech and never carried a rifle, whom we know as our brothers, though perhaps they know not us. Two I will name who live for ever, Shelley, the first of poets, were it not that there is one yet greater than he, the mystic William Blake. We are thought of as men of blood; we are hounded over the face of the globe. And who of our persecutors would believe that the song we bear in our hearts, some of us, I may speak at least for one, is the most inspired, the most spiritual challenge ever flung to your obtuse, flatulent, stertorous England:

> ' *Bring me my bow of burning gold,*
> *Bring me my arrows of desire,*
> *Bring me my spear; O clouds unfold!*
> *Bring me my chariot of fire!*
>
> *I will not cease from mental fight,*
> *Nor shall my sword sleep in my hand,*
> *Till I have built Jerusalem*
> *In England's green and pleasant land.*'

"England! No, not England, but Europe, America, the world! Where is Man, the new Man, there is our country. But the new Man is buried in the old; and wherever he struggles in his tomb, wherever he knocks we are there to help to deliver him. When the guards sleep, in the silence of the dawn, rises the crucified Christ. And the angel that sits at the grave is the angel of Anarchy."

THUS abruptly he brought to a close his extraordinary peroration, to which I fear the written word has done but poor justice. A long silence followed; in it there was borne to us from below the murmur of the hidden fountain, the wail of the nightingale. It was night now; the moon had set, and the sky was thick with stars. Among them one planet was blazing red, just opposite where I sat; and I saw the eyes of my neighbour, Henry Martin, fixed upon it. He was so lost in thought that he did not hear me at first when I asked him whether he would care to follow on. But he assented willingly enough as soon as he understood. And as he rose I could not help admiring, as I had often done before, the singular beauty of his countenance. His books, I think, do him injustice; they are cold and academic. But there was nothing of that in the man himself; never was spirit so alert; and that alertness was reflected in his person and bearing, his erect figure, his brilliant eyes, and the tumultuous sweep of his now whitening beard. He stood for a moment silent, with his eyes still fixed on the red star; then began to speak as follows:

"If," he said, "it be true, as certain mystics maintain, that the world is an effect of the antagonisms of spiritual beings, having their stations in opposite quarters of the heavens, then, I think, MacCarthy and myself must represent such a pair of contraries, and move in an antithetic balance through the cycle of experience. I, perhaps, am the Urthona of his prophet Blake, and he the Urizen, or vice versa, it may be, I cannot tell. But our opposition involves, on my part at least, no hostility; and looking across to his quarter of the sky I can readily conceive how proud a fate it must be to burn there, so red, so sumptuous, and so superb. My own light is pale by comparison, a mere green and blue; yet it is equally essential; and without it there might be a danger that he would consume the world. I speak in metaphors, that I may effect as gently as possible the necessary transition, so cold and abrupt, from the prophet to the critic. But you, sir, in calling upon me, knew what you were doing. You knew well that you were inviting Aquarius to empty his watering-pot on Mars. And Mars, I am sure, will pardon me if I obey. Unlike all the previous speakers, I am, by vocation, a sceptic; and the vocation I hold to be a noble one. There are people who think, perhaps, indeed, there is almost nobody who does not think, that action is the sole end of life. Criticism, they hold, is a kind of disease to which some people are subject, and which, in extreme cases, may easily be fatal. The healthy state, on the other hand, they think, is that of the enthusiast; of the man who believes and never doubts. Now, that such a state is happy I am very ready to admit; but I cannot hold that it is healthy. How could it be, unless it were based upon a sound, intellectual foundation? But no such foundation has been or will be reached except through criticism; and all criticism implies and engenders doubt. A man who has never experienced, nay, I will say who is not constantly reiterating, the process of criticism, is a man who has no right to his enthusiasm. For he has won it at the cost of drugging his mind with passion; and that I maintain is a bad and wrong thing. I maintain it to be bad and wrong in itself, and quite apart from any consequences it may produce; for it is a primary duty to seek what is true and eschew what is false. But even from the secondary point of view of consequences, I have the gravest doubts as to the common assumption that the effects of enthusiasm are always preponderantly if not wholly good. When I consider, for example, the history of religion, I find no warrant for affirming that its services have outweighed its disservices. Jesus Christ, the greatest and, I think, the sanest of enthusiasts, lit the fires of the Inquisition and set up the Pope at Rome. Mahomet deluged the earth with blood, and planted the Turk on the Bosphorus. Saint Francis created a horde of sturdy beggars. Luther declared the Thirty Years' War. Criticism would have arrested the course of these men; but would the world have been the worse? I doubt it. There would have been less heat; but there might have been more light. And, for my part, I believe in light. It may, indeed, be true that intellect without passion is barren; but it is certain that passion without intellect is mischievous. And since these powers, which should be united, are, in fact, at war in the great duel which runs through history, I take my stand with the intellect. If I must choose, I would rather be barren than mischievous. But it is my aim to be fruitful, and to be fruitful through criticism. That means, I fear, that I am bound to make myself unpleasant to everybody. But I do it, not of malice prepense, but as in duty bound. You will say, perhaps, that that only makes the matter worse. Well, so be it! I will apologize no more, but proceed at once to my disagreeable task.

"Let me say then first, that in listening to the speakers who have preceded me, while admiring the beauty and ingenuity of the superstructures they have raised, I have been busy, according to my practice, in questioning the foundations. And this is the kind of result I have arrived at. All political convictions vary between the two extremes which I will call Collectivism and Anarchy. Each of these pursues at all costs a certain end — Collectivism, order, and Anarchy, liberty. Each is held as a faith and propagated as a religion. And between them lie those various compromises between faith and experience, idea and fact, which are represented by liberalism, conservatism, and the like. Now, the degree of enthusiasm which accompanies a belief, is commonly in direct proportion to its freedom from empirical elements. Simplicity and immediacy are the characteristics of all passionate conviction. But a critic like myself cannot believe that in politics, or anywhere in the field of practical action, any such simple and immediate beliefs are really and wholly true. Thus, in the case before us, I would point out that neither liberty nor order are sufficient ends in themselves, though each, I think, is part of the end. The liberty that is desirable is that of good people pursuing Good in order; and the order that is desirable is that of good people pursuing Good in liberty. This is a correction which, perhaps, both collectivist and anarchist would accept. What they want, they would say, is that kind of liberty and that kind of order which I have described. But as liberty and order, so conceived, imply one another, the difference between the two positions ceases to be one of ends and becomes one of means. But every problem of means is one of extreme complexity which can only be solved, in the most tentative way, by observation and experiment. And opinions based upon such a process, though they may be strongly held, cannot be held with the simplicity and force of a religious or ethical intuition. We might, conceivably, on this basis adopt the position either of the collectivist or of the anarchist; but we should do so not as enthusiasts, but as critics, with a full consciousness that we are resting not upon an absolute principle, but upon a balance of probabilities.

"This, then, is the first point I wished to make, that the whole question is one to be attacked by criticism, not by intuition. But now, tested by criticism, both the extreme positions suggest the gravest possible difficulties and doubts. In the case of anarchy, especially, these force themselves upon the most superficial view. The anarchist maintains, in effect, that to bring about his ideal of ordered liberty all you have to do is to abolish government. But he can point to no experience that will justify such a belief. It is based upon a theory of human nature which is contradicted by all the facts known to us. For if men, were it not for government, might be living in the garden of Eden, how comes it that they ever emerged from that paradise? No, it is not government that is the root of our troubles, it is the niggardliness of Nature and the greed of man. And both these are primitive facts which would be strengthened, not destroyed, by anarchy. Can it be believed that the result would be satisfactory? The anarchist may indeed reply that anything would be better than what exists. And I can well understand how some generous and sensitive souls, or some victims of intolerable oppression, may be driven into such counsels. But they are surely counsels of despair! Or is it possible really to hold — as MacCarthy apparently does — that on the eve of a bloody revolution, whereby all owners of property will be summarily deprived of all they have, the friendly and co-operative instincts of human nature will immediately come into play without friction; that the infinitely complex problems of production and distribution will solve themselves, as it were, of their own accord; that there will be a place ready for everybody to do exactly the work he wants; that everybody will want to work at something, and will be contented with the wage assigned him; that there will be no shortage, no lack of adaptation of demand to supply; and all this achieved, not by virtue of any new knowledge or new capacity, but simply by a rearrangement of existing elements? Does any one, does MacCarthy really, in a calm moment, believe all this? And is he prepared to stake society upon his faith? If he be, he is indeed beyond the reach of my watering-pot. I leave him, therefore, burning luridly and unsubdued, and pass on to Allison.

"Allison's flame is gentler; and I would not wish, even if I could, altogether to extinguish it. But I am anxious, I confess, to temper it; for in colour, to my taste, it is a little ghastly; and I fear that if it increased in intensity, it might even become too hot, though I do not suggest that that is a present danger. To drop the metaphor, my objections to collectivism are not as fundamental as my objections to anarchy, nor are they based upon any lack of appreciation of the advantages of that more equitable distribution of the opportunities of life which I take to be at the bottom of the collectivist ideal. I do not share — no man surely who has reflected could share — the common prejudice that there is something fundamental, natural, and inevitable about the existing organization of property. On the contrary, it is clear to me that it is inequitable; and that the substitution of the system advocated by collectivists would be an immense improvement, if it could be successfully carried out, and if it did not endanger other Goods, which may be even more important than equality of opportunity. Nor do I hold that in a collectivist state there need be any dangerous relaxation of that motive of self-interest which every reasonable man must admit to be, up to a point, the most potent source of all practical energy. I do not see why the state should not pay its servants according to merit just as private companies do, and make the rewards of ambition depend on efficiency. In this purely economic region there is not, so it seems to me, anything absurd or chimerical in the socialist ideal. My difficulty here is of a different kind. I do not see how, by the democratic machinery contemplated, it will be possible to secure officials sufficiently competent and disinterested to be entrusted with functions so important and so difficult as those which would be demanded of them under the socialist régime. In a democracy the government can hardly rise above — in practice, I think, it tends to fall below — the average level of honesty and intelligence. In the United States, for example, it is notorious that the whole machinery of government, and especially of local government, where the economic functions are important, is exploited by the more unscrupulous members of the community; and this tendency must be immensely accentuated in every society in proportion as the functions of government become important. A socialist state badly administered would, I believe, be worse than the state under which we live, to the same degree in which, when well administered, it would be better. And I do not, I confess, see what guarantees socialists can offer that the administration will be good. I have far less confidence than Allison in mere machinery; and I am sure that no machinery will produce good results in a society where a large proportion of the citizens have no other idea than to exploit the powers of government in their own interest. But such, I believe, is the case in existing societies; and I do not see by what miracle they are going to be transformed.

" Such is my first difficulty with regard to collectivism. And though it would not prevent me from supporting, as in fact I do support, cautious and tentative experiments in the direction of practical socialism, it does prevent me from looking to a collectivist future with anything like the breezy confidence which animates Allison. And I will go further: I will say that no man who possesses an adequate intelligence, and does not deliberately stifle it, has a right to any such confidence. Setting aside, however, for the sake of argument, this difficulty, and admitting the possibility of an honest and efficient collectivist state, I am confronted with a further and even graver cause of hesitation. For while I consider that the distribution of the opportunities of life is, under the existing system, in the highest degree capricious and inequitable, yet I would prefer such inequity to the most equitable arrangement in the world if it afforded a better guarantee for the realization of certain higher goods than would be afforded by the improved system. And I am not clear in my own mind, and I do not see how any one can be clear, that collectivism gives as good a security as the present system for the realization of these higher goods. And this brings me back to the question of liberty. On this point there is, I am well aware, a great deal of cant talked, and I have no wish to add to it. Under our present arrangements, I admit, for the great mass of people, there is no liberty worth the name; seeing that they are bound and tied all their lives to the meanest necessities. And yet we see that out of the midst of all this chaos of wrong, there have emerged and do emerge artists, poets, men of science, saints. And the appearance of such men seems to me to depend on the fact that a considerable minority have the power to choose, for good or for evil, their own life, to follow their bent, even in the face of tremendous difficulties, and, perhaps because of those difficulties in the more fortunate cases, to realize, at whatever cost of suffering, great works and great lives. But under the system sketched by Allison I have the gravest doubts whether any man of genius would ever emerge. The very fact that everybody's career will be regulated for him, and his difficulties smoothed away, that, in a word, the open road will imply the beaten track, will, I fear, diminish, if not destroy, the enterprise, the innate spirit of adventure, in the spiritual as in the physical world, on which depends all that we call, or ought to call, progress. A collectivist state, it is true, might establish and endow academies; but would it ever produce a Shakspere or a Michelangelo? It might engender and foster religious orthodoxy; but would it have a place for the reformer or the saint? Should we not have to pay for the general level of comfort and intelligence, by suppressing the only thing good in itself, the manifestation of genius? I do not say dogmatically that it would be so: I do not even say dogmatically that, even if it were, the argument would be conclusive against the collectivist state. But the issue is so tremendous that it necessarily makes me pause, as it must, I contend, any candid man, who is not prejudiced by a preconceived ideal.

"Now, it is not for the sake of recommending any opinion of my own that I have dwelt on these considerations. It is, rather, to illustrate and drive home the point with which I began, that the intellect has its rights, that it enters into every creed, and that it undermines, in every creed, all elements of mere irrational or antirational faith; that this fact can only be disguised by a conscious or unconscious predetermination, not to let the intellect have its say; and that such predetermination is a very serious error and vice. It is without shame and without regret, on the contrary it is with satisfaction and self-approval, that I find in my own case, my intelligence daily more and more undermining my instinctive beliefs. If, as some

[74]

have held, it were necessary to choose between reason and passion, I would choose reason. But I find no such necessity; for reason to me herself is a passion. Men think the life of reason cold. How little do they know what it is to be responsive to every call, solicited by every impulse, yet still, like the magnet, vibrate ever to the north, never so tense, never so aware of the stress and strain of force as when most irremovably fixed upon that goal. The intensity of life is not to be measured by the degree of oscillation. It is at the stillest point that the most tremendous energies meet; and such a point is the intelligence open to infinity. For such stillness I feel myself to be destined, if ever I could attain it. But others, I suppose, like Mac-Carthy, have a different fate. In the celestial world of souls, the hierarchy of spirits, there is need of the planet no less than of its sun. The station and gravity of the one determines the orbit of the other, and the antagonism that keeps them apart also knits them together. There is no motion of MacCarthy's but I vibrate to it; and about my immobility he revolves. But both of us, as I am inclined to think, are included in a larger system and move together on a remoter centre. And the very law of our contention, as perhaps one day we may come to see, is that of a love that by discord achieves harmony."

THE conclusion of Martin's speech left me somewhat in doubt how to proceed. All of the company who were primarily interested in politics had now spoken; and I was afraid there might be a complete break in the subject of our discourse. Casting about, I could think of nothing better than to call upon Wilson, the biologist. For though he was a specialist, he regarded everything as a branch of his specialty; and would, I knew, be as ready to discourse on society as on anything else. Although, therefore, I disliked a certain arrogance he was wont to display, I felt that, since he was to speak, this was the proper place to introduce him. I asked him accordingly to take up the thread of the debate; and without pause his aggressive voice began to assail our ears.

"I don't quite know," he began, "why a mere man of science should be invited to intervene in a debate on these high subjects. Politics, I have always understood, is a kind of mystery, only to be grasped by a favoured few, and then not by any processes of thought, but by some kind of intuition. But of late years something seems to have happened. The intuition theory was all very well when the intuitions did not conflict, or when, at least, those who were possessed by one, never came into real intellectual contact with those who were possessed by another. But here, to-night, have we met together upon this terrace, been confronted with the most opposite principles jostling in the roughest way, and, as it seems to the outsider, simply annihilating one another. Whence Martin's plea for criticism; a plea with which I most heartily sympathize, only that he gave no indication of the basis on which criticism itself is to rest. And perhaps that is where and why I come in. I have been watching to-night with curiosity, and I must confess with a little amusement, one building after another laboriously raised by each speaker in turn, only to collapse ignominiously at the first touch administered by his successor. And why? For the ancient reason, that the structures were built upon the sand. Well, I have raised no building myself to speak of. But I am one of an obscure group of people who are working at solid foundations; which is only another way of saying that I am a man of science. Only a biologist, it is true; heaven forfend that I should call myself a sociologist! But biology is one of the disciplines that are building up that general view of Nature and the world which is gradually revolutionizing all our social conceptions. The politicians, I am afraid, are hardly aware of this. And that is why — if I may say so without offence — their utterances are coming to seem more and more a kind of irrelevant prattle. The forces that really move the world have passed out of their control. And it is only where the forces are at work that the living ideas move upon the waters. Politicians don't study science; that is the extraordinary fact. And yet every day it becomes clearer that politics is either an applied science or a charlatanism. Only, unfortunately, as the most important things are precisely the last to be known about, and it is exactly where it is most imperative to act that our ignorance is most complete, the science of politics has hardly yet even begun to be studied. Hence our forlorn paralysis of doubt whenever we pause to reflect; and hence the kind of blind desperation with which earnest people are impelled to rush incontinently into practice. The position of MacCarthy is very intelligible, however much it be, to my mind,— what shall I say ? — regrettable. There is, in fact, hardly a question that has been raised to-night that is at present capable of scientific determination. And with that word I ought perhaps, in my capacity of man of science, to sit down.

"And so I would, if it were not that there is something else, besides positive conclusions, that results from a long devotion to science. There is a certain attitude towards life, a certain sense of what is important and what is not, a view of what one may call the commonplaces of existence, that distinguishes, I think, all competent people who have been trained in that discipline. For we do think about politics, or rather about society, even we specialists. And between us we are gradually developing a sort of body of first principles which will be at the basis of any future sociology. It is these that I feel tempted to try to indicate. And the more so, because they are so foreign to much that has been spoken here to-night. I have had a kind of feeling, to tell the truth, throughout this whole discussion, of dwelling among the tombs and listening to the voices of the dead. And I feel a kind of need to speak for the living, for the new generation with which I believe I am in touch. I want to say how the problems you have raised look to us, who live in the dry light of physical science.

"Let me say, then, to begin with, that for us the nineteenth century marks a breach with the whole past of the world to which there is nothing comparable in human annals. We have developed wholly new powers; and, coincidentally and correspondingly, a wholly new attitude to life. Of the powers I do not intend to speak; the wonders of steam and electricity are the hackneyed theme of every halfpenny paper. But the attitude to life, which is even more important, is something that has hardly yet been formulated. And I shall endeavour to give some first rough expression to it.

"The first constituent, then, of the new view is that of continuity. We of the new generation realize that the present is a mere transition from the past into the future; that no event and no moment is isolated; that all things, successive as well as coinci-

dent, are bound in a single system. Of this system
the general formula is causation. But, in human
society, the specifically important case of it is the
nexus of successive generations. We do not now,
we who reflect, regard man as an individual, nor
even as one of a body of contemporaries; we regard
him as primarily a son and a father. In other words,
what we have in mind is always the race; whereas
hitherto the central point has been the individual
or the citizen. But this shifting in the point of view
implies a revolution in ethics and politics. With the
ancients, the maintenance of the existing generation
was the main consideration, and patriotism its formula. To Marcus Aurelius, to the Stoics, as later to
the Christians, the subject of all moral duties was
the individual soul, and personal salvation became
for centuries the corner-stone of the ethical structure. Well, all the speculation, all the doctrine, all
the literature based upon that conception has become irrelevant and meaningless in the light of the
new ideal. We no longer conceive the individual
save as one in a chain of births. Fatherless, he is in-
conceivable; sonless, he is abortive. His soul, if he
have one, is inseparable from its derivation from

the past and its tradition to the future. His duty, his happiness, his value, are all bound up with the fact of paternity; and the same, *mutatis mutandis*, is true of women. The new generation in a word has a totally new code of ethics; and that code is directed to the end of the perfection of the race. For, and this is the second constituent of the modern view, the series of births is also the vehicle of progress. It is this discovery that gives to our outlook on life its exhilaration and zest. The ancients conceived the Golden Age as lying in the past; the men of the Middle Ages removed it to an imaginary heaven. Both in effect despaired of this world; and consequently their characteristic philosophy is that of the tub or the hermitage. So soon as the first flush of youth was past, pessimism clouded the civilization of Greece and of Rome; and from this Christianity escaped only to take refuge in an imaginary bliss beyond the grave. But we, by means of science, have established progress. We look to a future, a future assured, and a future in this world. Our eyes are on the coming generations; in them centres our hope and our duty. To feed them, to clothe them, to educate them, to make them better than ourselves, to do for them all that has hitherto been so scandalously neglected, and in doing it to find our own life and our own satisfaction — that is our task and our privilege, ours of the new generation.

"And this brings me to the third point in our scheme of life. We believe in progress; but we do not believe that progress is fated. And here, too, our outlook is essentially new. Hitherto, the conceptions of Fate and Providence have divided the empire of the world. We of the new generation accept neither. We believe neither in a good God directing the course of events; nor in a blind power that controls them independently and in despite of human will. We know that what we do or fail to do matters. We know that we have will; that will may be directed by reason; and that the end to which reason points is the progress of the race. This much we hold to be established; more than this we do not need. And it is the acceptance of just this that cuts us off from the past, that makes its literature, its ethics, its politics, meaningless and unintelligible to us, that makes us, in a word, what we are, the first of the new generation.

" Well, now, assuming this standpoint let us go on to see how some of the questions look which have been touched upon to-night. Those questions have been connected mainly with government and property. And upon these two factors, it would seem, in the opinion of previous speakers, all the interests of society turn. But from the point where we now stand we see clearly that there is a third factor to which these are altogether subordinate — I mean the family. For the family is the immediate agent in the production and rearing of children; and this, as we have seen, is the end of society. With the family therefore social reconstruction should start. And we may lay down as the fundamental ethical and social axiom that everybody not physically disqualified ought to marry, and to produce at least four children. The only question here is whether the state should intervene and endeavour so to regulate marriages as to bring together those whose union is most likely to result in good offspring. This is a point on which the ancients, I am aware, in their light-hearted sciolism laid great stress. Only, characteristically enough, they ignored the fundamental difficulty, that nothing is known —

nothing even now, and how much less then! — of the conditions necessary to produce the desired result. If ever the conditions should come to be understood — and the problem is pre-eminently one for science; and if ever what is even more difficult — we should come to know clearly and exactly for what points we ought to breed; then, no doubt, it may be desirable for government to undertake the complete regulation of marriage. Meantime, we must confine our efforts to the simpler and more manageable task of securing for the children when they are born the best possible environment, physical, intellectual and moral. But this may be done, even without a radical reconstruction of the law of property, simply by proceeding further on the lines on which we are already embarked, by insisting on a certain standard, and that a high one, of house-room, sanitation, food, and the like. We could thus ensure from the beginning for every child at least a sound physical development; and that without undermining the responsibility of parents. What else the state can do, it must do by education; a thing which, at present, I do not hesitate to say, does not exist among us.

We have an elementary system of cram and drill directed by the soulless automata it has itself produced; a secondary system of athletics and dead languages presided over by gentlemanly amateurs; and a university system which — well, of which I cannot trust myself to speak. I wish only to indicate that, in the eyes of the new generation, breeding and education are the two cardinal pillars of society. All other questions, even those of property and government, are subordinate; and only as subordinate can they be fruitfully approached. Take, for example, property. On this point we have no prejudices, either socialistic or anti-socialistic. Property, as we view it, is simply a tool for producing and perfecting men. Whether it will serve that purpose best if controlled by individuals or by the state, or partly by the one and partly by the other, we regard as an open question, to be settled by experiment. We see no principle one way or the other. Property is not a right, nor a duty, nor a privilege, either of individuals or of the community. It is simply and solely, like everything else, a function of the chain of births. Whoever owns it, however it is administered, it has only one object, to ensure for every child that is born a sufficiency of physical goods, and for the better-endowed all that they require in the way of training to enable them to perform efficiently the higher duties of society.

"And as property is merely a means, so is government. To us of the new generation nothing is more surprising and more repugnant, than the importance attached by politicians to formulæ which have long since lost whatever significance they may once have possessed. Democracy, representation, trust in the people and the rest, all this to us is the idlest verbiage. It is notorious, even to those who make most play with these phrases, that the people do not govern themselves, that they cannot do so, and that they would make a great mess of it if they could. The truth is, that we are living politically on a tradition which arose when by government was meant government by a class, when one man or a few exploited the rest in the name of the state, and when therefore it was of imperative importance to bring to bear upon those who were in power the brute and unintelligent weight of the mass. The whole democratic movement, though it assumed a positive intellectual form, was in fact negative in its aim and scope. It meant simply, we will not be exploited. But that end has now been attained. There is no fear now that government will be oppressive; and the only problem of the future is, how to make it efficient. But efficiency, it is certain, can never be secured by democratic machinery. We must, as Allison rightly maintains, have trained and skilled persons. How these are to be secured is a matter of detail, though no doubt of important detail; and it is one that the new generation will have to solve. What they will want, in any case, is government. MacCarthy's idea of anarchy is — well, if he will pardon my saying so, it is hardly worthy of his intelligence. You cannot regulate society, any more than you can spin cotton, by the light of nature and a good heart. MacCarthy mistakes the character of government altogether, when he imagines its essence to be compulsion. Its essence is direction; and direction, whatever the form of society, is, or should be, reserved for the wise. It is for wise direction that the coming generations cry; and it is our business to see that they get it.

"I have thus indicated briefly the view of social and political questions which I believe will be that of the future. And my reason for thinking so is, that that view is based upon science. It is this that distinguishes the new generation from all others. Hitherto the affairs of the world have been conducted by passion, interest, sentiment, religion, anything but reasoned knowledge. The end of that régime, which has dominated all history, is at hand. The old influences, it is true, still survive, and even appear to be supreme. We have had ample evidence to-night of their apparent vitality. But underneath them is growing up the sturdy plant of science. Already it has dislodged their roots; and though they still seem to bear flower, the flower is withering before our eyes. In its place, before long, will appear the new and splendid blossom whose appearance ends and begins an epoch of evolution. That is a consummation nothing can delay. We need not fret or hurry. We have only to work on silently at the foundations. The city, it is true, seems to be rising apart from our labours. There, in the distance, are the stately buildings, there is the noise of the masons, the carpenters, the engineers. But see! the whole structure shakes and trembles as it grows. Houses fall as fast as they are erected; foundations sink, towers settle, domes and pinnacles collapse. All history is the building of a dream-city, fantastic as that ancient one of the birds, changeful as the sunset clouds. And no wonder; for it is building on the sand. There is only one foundation of rock, and that is being laid by science. Only wait! To us will come sooner or later, the people and the architects. To us they will submit the great plans they have striven so vainly to realize. We shall pronounce on their possibility, their suitability, even their beauty. Cæsar and Napoleon will give place to Comte and Herbert Spencer; and Newton and Darwin sit in judgment on Plato and Aquinas."

WITH that he concluded. And as he sat down a note was passed along to me from Ellis, asking permision to speak next. I assented willingly; for Ellis, though some of us thought him frivolous, was, at any rate, never dull. His sunburnt complexion, his fair curly hair, and the light in his blue eyes made a pleasant impression, as he rose and looked down upon us from his six feet.

"This," he began, " is really an extraordinary

discovery Wilson has made, that fathers have children, and children fathers! One wonders how the world has got on all these centuries in ignorance of it. It seems so obvious, once it has been stated. But that, of course, is the nature of great truths; as soon as they are announced they seem to have been always familiar. It is possible, for that very reason, that many people may underestimate the importance of Wilson's pronouncement, forgetting that it is the privilege of genius to formulate for the first time what every one has been dimly feeling. We ought not to be ungrateful; but perhaps it is our duty to be cautious. For great ideas naturally suggest practical applications, and it is here that I foresee difficulties. What Wilson's proposition in fact amounts to, if I understand him rightly, is that we ought to open as wide as possible the gates of life, and make those who enter as comfortable as we can. Now, I think we ought to be very careful about doing anything of the kind. We know, of course, very little about the conditions of the unborn. But I think it highly probable that, like labour, as described by the political economists, they form throughout the universe a single mobile body, with a tendency to gravitate wherever the access is freest and the conditions most favourable. And I should be very much afraid of attracting what we may call, perhaps, the unemployed of the universe in undue proportions to this planet, by offering them artificially better terms than are to be obtained elsewhere. For that, as you know, would defeat our own object. We should merely cause an exodus, as it were, from the outlying and rural districts, Mars, or the moon, or whatever the place may be; and the amount of distress and difficulty on the earth would be greater than ever. At any rate, I should insist, and I daresay Wilson agrees with me there, on some adequate test. And I would not advertise too widely what we are doing. After all, other planets must be responsible for their own unborn; and I don't see why we should become a kind of dumping-ground of the universe for every one who may imagine he can better himself by migrating to the earth. For that reason among others, I would not open the gate too wide. And, perhaps, in view of this consideration, we might still permit some people not to marry. At any rate, I would n't go further, I think, than a fine for recalcitrant bachelors. Wilson, I daresay, would prefer imprisonment for a second offence, and in case of contumacy, even capital punishment. On such a point I am not, I confess, an altogether impartial judge, as I should certainly incur the greater penalty. Still, as I have said, in the general interests of society, and in view of the conditions of the universal market, I would urge caution and deliberation. And that is all I have to say at present on this very interesting subject.

" The other point that interested me in Wilson's remarks was not, indeed, so novel as the discovery about fathers having children, but it was, in its way, equally important. I mean, the announcement made with authority that the human race really does, as has been so often conjectured, progress. We may take it now, I suppose, that that is established, or Wilson would not have proclaimed it. And we are, therefore, in a position roughly to determine in what progress consists. This is a task which, I believe, I am more competent to attempt perhaps even than Wilson himself, because I have had unusual opportunities of travel, and have endeavoured to utilize them to clear my mind of prejudices. I flatter myself that I can regard with perfect impartiality the ideals of different countries, and in particular those of the new world which, I presume, are to dominate the future. In attempting to estimate what progress means, one could not do better, I suppose, than describe the civilization of the United States. For in describing that, one will be describing the whole civilization of the future, seeing that what America is our colonies are, or will become, and what our colonies are we, too, may hope to attain, if we make the proper sacrifices to preserve the unity of the empire. Let us see, then, what, from an objective point of view, really is the future of this progressing world of ours.

"Perhaps, however, before proceeding to analyse the spiritual ideals of the American people, I had better give some account of their country. For environment, as we all know now, has an incalculable effect upon character. Consider, then, the American continent! How simple it is! How broad! How large! How grand in design! A strip of coast, a range of mountains, a plain, a second range, a second strip of coast! That is all! Contrast the complexity of Europe, its lack of symmetry, its variety, irregularity, disorder and caprice! The geography of the two continents already foreshadows the differences in their civilizations. On the one hand simplicity and size; on the other a hole-and-corner variety: there immense rivers, endless forests, interminable plains, indefinite repetition of a few broad ideas; here distracting transitions, novelties, surprises, shocks, distinctions in a word, already suggesting Distinction. Even in its physical features America is the land of quantity, while Europe is that of quality. And as with the land, so with its products. How large are the American fruits! How tall the trees! How immense the oysters! What has Europe by comparison? Mere flavour and form, mere beauty, delicacy and grace! America, one would say, is the latest work of the great artist -- we are told, indeed, by geologists, that it is the youngest of the continents -- conceived at an age when he had begun to repeat himself, broad, summary, impressionist, audacious in empty space; whereas Europe would seem to represent his pre-Raphaelite period, in its wealth of detail, its variety of figure, costume, architecture, landscape, its crudely contrasted colours and minute precision of individual form.

"And as with the countries, so with their civilizations. Europe is the home of class, America of democracy. By democracy I do not mean a mere form of government — in that respect, of course, America is less democratic than England; I mean the mental attitude that implies and engenders Indistinction. Indistinction, I say, rather than equality, for the word equality is misleading, and might seem to imply, for example, a social and economic parity of conditions, which no more exists in America than it does in Europe. Politically, as well as socially, America is a plutocracy; her democracy is spiritual and intellectual; and its essence is, the denial of all superiorities save that of wealth. Such superiorities, in fact, hardly exist across the Atlantic. All men there are intelligent, all efficient, all energetic; and as these are the only qualities they possess, so they are the only ones they feel called upon to admire. How different is the case with Europe! How innumerable and how confusing the gradations! For diversities of language and race, indeed, we may not be altogether responsible; but we have superadded to these, distinctions of manner, of feeling, of perception, of intellectual grasp and spiritual insight, unknown to the simpler and vaster consciousness of the West. In addition, in short, to the obvious and fundamentally natural standard of wealth, we have invented others impalpable and artificial in their character; and however rapidly these may be destined to disappear as the race progresses, and the influence of the West begins to dominate the East, they do, nevertheless, still persist, and give to our effete civilization the character of Aristocracy, that is of Caste. In all this we see, as I have suggested, the influence of environment. The old-world stock, transplanted across the ocean, imitates the characteristics of its new home. Sloughing off artificial distinctions, it manifests itself in bold simplicity, broad as the plains, turbulent as the rivers, formless as the mountains, crude as the fruits of its adopted country.

Yet while thus forming themselves into the image of the new world, the Americans have not disdained to make use of such acquisitions of the Past as might be useful to them in the task that lay before them. They have rejected our ideals and our standards; but they have borrowed our capital and our inventions. They have thus been able -- a thing unknown before in the history of the world — to start the battle against Nature with weapons ready forged. On the material results they have thus been able to achieve it is the less necessary for me to dilate, that they keep us so fully informed of them themselves. But it may be interesting to note an important consequence in their spiritual life, which has commonly escaped the notice of observers. Thanks to Europe, America has never been powerless in the face of Nature; therefore has never felt Fear; therefore never known Reverence; and therefore never experienced Religion. It may seem paradoxical to make such an assertion about the descendants of the Puritan Fathers; nor do I forget the notorious fact that America is the home of the sects, from the followers of Joseph Smith to those of Mrs. Eddy. But these are the phenomena that illustrate my point. A nation which knew what religion was, in the European sense; whose roots were struck in the soil of spiritual conflict, of temptations and visions in haunted forests or desert sands by the Nile, of midnight risings, scourgings of the flesh, dirges in vast cathedrals, and the miracle of the Host solemnly veiled in a glory of painted light — such a nation would never have accepted Christian Science as a religion. No! Religion in America is a parasite without roots. The questions that have occupied Europe from the dawn of her history, for which she has fought more fiercely than for empire or liberty, for which she has fasted in deserts, agonized in cells, suffered on the cross, and at the stake, for which she has sacrificed wealth, health, ease, intelligence, life, these questions of the meaning of the world, the origin and destiny of the soul, the life after death, the existence of God, and his relation to the universe, for the American people simply do not exist. They are as inaccessible, as impossible to them, as the Sphere to the dwellers in Flatland. That whole dimension is unknown to them. Their healthy and robust intelligence confines itself to the things of this world. Their religion, if they have one, is what I believe they call 'healthy-mindedness'. It consists in ignoring everything that

might suggest a doubt as to the worth of existence, and so conceivably paralyse activity. 'Let
us eat and drink,' they say, with a hearty and
robust good faith; omitting as irrelevant and
morbid the discouraging appendix, 'for to-morrow we die.' Indeed! What has death to do with
buildings twenty-four stories high, with the fast-
est trains, the noisiest cities, the busiest crowds in
the world, and generally the largest, the finest, the
most accelerated of everything that exists? America has sloughed off religion; and as, in the history of Europe, religion has underlain every other
activity, she has sloughed off, along with it, the
whole European system of spiritual life. Literature, for instance, and Art, do not exist across the
Atlantic. I am aware, of course, that Americans
write books and paint pictures. But their books are
not Literature, nor their pictures Art, except in so
far as they represent a faint adumbration of the
European tradition. The true spirit of America
has no use for such activities. And even if, as must
occasionally happen in a population of eighty mil-
lions, there is born among them a man of artistic
instincts, he is immediately and inevitably repelled

to Europe, whence he derives his training and his inspiration, and where alone he can live, observe and create. That this must be so from the nature of the case is obvious when we reflect that the spirit of Art is disinterested contemplation, while that of America is cupidous acquisition. Americans, I am aware, believe that they will produce Literature and Art, as they produce coal and steel and oil, by the judicious application of intelligence and capital; but here they do themselves injustice. The qualities that are making them masters of the world, unfit them for slighter and less serious pursuits. The Future is for them, the kingdom of elevators, of telephones, of motor-cars, of flying-machines. Let them not idly hark back, misled by effete traditions, to the old European dream of the kingdom of heaven. ' *Excudent alii* ' let them say, 'for Europe, Letters and Art; *tu regere argento populos, Morgane, memento*, let America rule the world by Syndicates and Trusts!' For such is her true destiny; and that she conceives it to be such, is evidenced by the determination with which she has suppressed all irrelevant activities. Every kind of disinterested intellectual operation she has severely repudiated. In Europe we take delight in the operations of the mind as such, we let it play about a subject, merely for the fun of the thing; we approve knowledge for its own sake; we appreciate irony and wit. But all this is unknown in America. The most intelligent people in the world, they severely limit their intelligence to the adaptation of means to ends. About the ends themselves they never permit themselves to speculate; and for this reason, though they calculate, they never think, though they invent, they never discover, and though they talk, they never converse. For thought implies speculation; reflection, discovery; conversation, leisure; and all alike imply a disinterestedness which has no place in the American system. For the same reason they do not play; they have converted games into battles; and battles in which every weapon is legitimate so long as it is victorious. An American foot-ball match exhibits in a type the American spirit, short, sharp, scientific, intense, no loitering by the road, no enjoyment of the process, no favour, no quarter, but a fight to the death with victory as the end, and anything and everything as the means.

A nation so severely practical could hardly be expected to attach the same importance to the emotions as has been attributed to them by Europeans. Feeling, like Intellect, is not regarded, in the West, as an end in itself. And it is not uninteresting to note that the Americans are the only great nation that have not produced a single lyric of love worth recording. Physically, as well as spiritually, they are a people of cold temperament. Their women, so much and, I do not doubt, so legitimately admired, are as hard as they are brilliant; their glitter is the glitter of ice. Thus happily constituted, Americans are able to avoid the immense waste of time and energy involved in the formation and maintenance of subtle personal relations. They marry, of course, they produce children, they propagate the race; but, I would venture to say, they do not love, as Europeans have loved; they do not exploit the emotion, analyse and enjoy it, still less express it in manners, in gesture, in epigram, in verse. And hence the kind of shudder produced in a cultivated European by the treatment of emotion in American fiction. The authors are trying to express something they have never experienced, and to graft the European tradition on to a civilization which has none of the elements necessary to nourish and support it.

"From this brief analysis of the attitude of Americans towards life, the point with which I started will, I hope, have become clear, that it is idle to apply to them any of the tests which we apply to a European civilization. For they have rejected, whether they know it or not, our whole scheme of values. What, then, is their own ? What do they recognize as an end ? This is an interesting point on which I have reflected much in the course of my travels. Sometimes I have thought it was wealth, sometimes power, sometimes activity. But a poem, or at least a production in metre, which I came across in the States, gave me a new idea upon the subject. On such a point I speak with great diffidence; but I am inclined to think that my author was right; that the real end which Americans set before themselves is Acceleration. To be always moving, and always moving faster, that they think is the beatific life; and with their happy detachment from philosophy and speculation,

they are not troubled by the question, Whither?
If they are asked by Europeans, as they sometimes are, what is the point of going so fast? their
only feeling is one of genuine astonishment. Why,
they reply, you go fast! And what more can be
said? Hence, their contempt for the leisure so
much valued by Europeans. Leisure they feel, to be
a kind of standing still, the unpardonable sin.
Hence, also, their aversion to play, to conversation,
to everything that is not work. I once asked an American who had been describing to me the scheme
of his laborious life, where it was that the fun came
in? He replied, without hesitation and without regret, that it came in nowhere. How should it? It
could only act as a brake; and a brake upon Acceleration is the last thing tolerable to the American genius.

"The American genius, I say: but after all, and
this is the real point of my remarks, what America is Europe is becoming. We, who sit here, with
the exception, of course, of Wilson, represent the
Past, not the Future. Politicians, professors, law-
yers, doctors, no matter what our calling, our
judgments are determined by the old scale of

values. Intellect, Beauty, Emotion, these are the things we count precious; to wealth and to progress we are indifferent, save as conducing to these. And thus, like the speakers who preceded me, we venture to criticise and doubt, where the modern man, American or European, simply and wholeheartedly accepts. For this it would be idle for us to blame ourselves, idle even to regret; we should simply and objectively note that we are out of court. All that we say may be true, but it is irrelevant. 'True,' says the man of the Future, 'we have no religion, literature, or art; we don't know whence we come, nor whither we go; but, what is more important, we don't care. What we do know is, that we are moving faster than any one ever moved before; and that there is every chance of our moving faster and faster. To inquire "whither" is the one thing that we recognize as blasphemous. The principle of the Universe is Acceleration, and we are its exponents; what is not accelerated will be extinguished; and if we cannot answer ultimate questions, that is the less to be regretted in that, a few centuries hence, there will be nobody left to ask them.'

"Such is the attitude which I believe to be that of the Future, both in the West and in the East. I do not pretend to sympathize with it; but my perception of it gives a peculiar piquancy to my own position. I rejoice that I was born at the end of an epoch; that I stand as it were at the summit, just before the plunge into the valley below; and looking back, survey and summarize in a glance the ages that are past. I rejoice that my friends are Socrates and Plato, Dante, Michelangelo, Goethe instead of Mr. Carnegie and Mr. Pierpont Morgan. I rejoice that I belong to an effete country; and that I sit at table with almost the last representatives of the culture, the learning and the ideals of centuries of civilization. I prefer the tradition of the Past to that of the Future; I value it the more for its contrast with that which is to come; and I am the more at ease inasmuch as I feel myself divested of all responsibility towards generations whose ideals and standards I am unable to appreciate.

"All this shows, of course, merely that I am not one of the people so aptly described by Wilson as the 'new generation.' But I flatter myself that my intellectual apprehension is not coloured by the circumstances of my own case, and that I have given you a clear and objective picture of what it is that really constitutes progress. And with that proud consciousness in my mind, I resume my seat."

THE conclusion of this speech was greeted with a hubbub of laughter, approval, and protest confusedly mixed; in the midst of which it occurred to me that I would select Audubon as the next speaker. My reason was that Ellis, as I thought, under cover of an extravagant fit of spleen, had made rather a formidable attack on the doctrine of progress as commonly understood by social reformers. He had given us, as it were, the first notes of the Negative. But Audubon, I knew, would play the tune through to the end; and I thought we might as well have it all, and have it before it should be too late for the possible correctives of other speakers. Audubon was engaged in some occupation in the city, and how he came to be a member of our society I cannot tell; for he professed an uncompromising aversion to all speculation. He was, however, a regular attendant and spoke well, though always in the sense that there was nothing worth speaking about. On this occasion he displayed, as usual, some reluctance to get on to his feet; and even when he was overruled began, characteristically, with a protest.

"I don't see why it should be a rule that everybody must speak. I believe I have said something of the kind before " — but here he was interrupted by a general exclamation that he had said it much too often; whereupon he dropped the subject, but maintained his tone of protest. "You don't understand, " he went on, " what a difficult position I am in, especially in a discussion of this kind. My standpoint is radically different from that of the rest of you; and anything I say is bound to be out of key. You 're all playing what you think to be the game of life, and playing it willingly. But I play only under compulsion; if you call it playing, when one is hounded out to field in all weathers without ever having a chance of an innings. Or, rather, the game 's more like tennis than cricket, and we 're the little boys who pick up the balls — and that, in my opinion, is a damned humiliating occupation.

And surely you must all really think so too! Of course, you don't like to admit it. Nobody does. In the pulpit, in the press, in conversation, even, there's a conspiracy of silence and bluff. It's only in rare moments, when a few men get together in the smoking-room, that the truth comes out. But when it does come out it's always the same refrain, 'cui bono, cui bono?' I don't take much account of myself; but, if there is one thing of which I am proud, it is that I have never let myself be duped. From the earliest days I can remember I realized what the nature of this world really is. And all experience has confirmed that first intuition. That other people don't seem to have it, too, is a source of constant amazement to me. But really, and without wishing to be arrogant, I believe the reason is that they choose to be duped and I don't. They intend, at all costs, to be happy, or interested, or whatever it is that they prefer to call it. And I don't say they are not wise in their generation. But I 'm not made like that; I just see things as they are; and I see that they 're very bad — a point in which I differ from the Creator.

"Well, now, to come to to-night's discussion,

and my attitude towards it. You have assumed throughout, as, of course, you were bound to do, that things are worth while. But if they are n't, what becomes of all your aims, all your views, all your problems and disputes? The basis on which you are all agreed, however much you may differ in detail, is that things can be made better, and that it's worth while to make them so. But if one denies both propositions, what happens to the superstructure? And I do deny them; and not only that, but I can't conceive how any one ever came to accept them. Surely, if one did n't approach the question with an irrational basis towards optimism, one would never imagine that there is such a thing as progress in anything that really matters. Or, are even we here impressed by such silly and irrelevant facts as telephones and motor-cars? Ellis, I should think, has said enough to dispel that kind of illusion; and I don't want to labour a tedious point. If we are to look for progress at all we must look for it, I suppose, in men. And I have never seen any evidence that men are generally better than they used to be; on the contrary, I think there is evidence that they are worse. But anyhow, even granting that we could make things a bit better, what would be the use of doing it in a world like this ? If the whole structure of the universe is bad, what 's the good of fiddling with the details ? You might as well waste your time in decorating the saloon of a sinking ship. Granting that you can improve the distribution of property, and raise the standard of health and intelligence and all the rest of it, granting you could to-morrow introduce your socialist state, or your liberal state, or your anarchical co-operation, or whatever the plan may be -- how would you be better off in anything that matters ? The main governing facts would be unaltered. Men, for example, would still be born, without being asked whether they want it or no. And that alone, to my mind, is enough to condemn the whole business. I can't think how it is that people don't resent more than they do the mere insult to their self-respect involved in such a situation. Nothing can cure it, nothing can improve it. It 's a fundamental condition of life.

"If that were all it would be bad enough. But that 's only the beginning. For the world into which we are thus ignominiously flung turns out to be in-calculable and irrational. There are, of course, I know, what are called the laws of nature. But I — to tell the honest truth — I don't believe in them. I mean, I see no reason to suppose that the sun will rise to-morrow, or that the seasons will continue to observe their course, or that any of our most certain expectations will be fulfilled in the future as they have been in the past. We import into the universe our own prejudice in favour of order; and the universe, I admit, up to a point appears to conform to it. But I don't trust the conformity. Too many evidences abound of frivolous and incalculable caprice. Why should not the appearance of order be but one caprice the more, or even a crowning device of calculated malice? And anyhow, the things that most concern us, tempests, epidemics, accidents, from the catastrophe of birth to the deliverance of death, we have no power to foresee or to forestall. Yet, in face of all this, borne home to us every hour of every day, we cling to the creed of universal law; and on the flux of chaos write our 'credo quia impossibile.'

"Well, that is a heresy of mine I have never

found any one to share. But no matter. My case is so strong I can afford to give it away point by point. Granting then, that there were order in the universe, how does that make it any better? Does it not rather make it worse, if the order is such as to produce evil? And how great that evil is I need not insist. For it has been presupposed in everything that has been said to-night. If it were a satisfactory world you would n't all be wanting to alter it. Still, you may say — people always do — 'if there is evil there is also good.' But it is just the things people call good, even more than those they admit to be evil, that make me despair of the world. How any one with self-respect can accept, and accept thankfully, the sort of things people do accept is to me a standing mystery. It is surely the greatest triumph achieved by the Power that made the universe that every week there gather into the Churches congregations of victims to recite their gratitude for 'their creation, preservation, and all the blessings of this life.' The blessings! What are they? Money? Success? Reputation? I don't profess, myself, to be anything better than a man of the world; but that those things should be valued as they are by men of the world is a thing that passes my understanding. 'Well, but,' says the moralist 'there's always duty and work.' But what is the value of work if there's nothing worth working for? 'Ah, but,' says the poet, 'there's beauty and love.' But the beauty and love he seeks is something he never finds. What he grasps is the shadow, not the thing. And even the shadow flits past and eludes him on the stream of time.

"And just there is the final demonstration of the malignity of the scheme of things. Time itself works against us. The moments that are evil it eternalizes; the moments that might be good it hurries to annihilation. All that is most precious is most precarious. Vainly do we cry to the moment: 'Verweile doch, du bist so schön!' Only the heavy hours are heavy-footed. The winged Psyche, even at the moment of birth, is sick with the pangs of dissolution.

"These, surely, are facts, not imaginations. Why, then, is it that men refuse to look them in the face? Or, if they do, turn at once away to construct some other kind of world? For that is the most extraordinary thing of all, that men invent systems, and that those systems are optimistic. It is as though they said: 'Things must be good. But as they obviously are not good, they must really be other than they are.' And hence these extraordinary doctrines, so pitiful, so pathetic, so absurd, of the eternal good God who made this bad world, of the Absolute whose only manifestation is the Relative, of the Real which has so much less reality than the Phenomenal. Or, if all that be rejected, we transfer our heaven from eternity to time, and project into the future the perfection we miss in the present or in the past. 'True,' we say, 'a bad world! but then how good it will be!' And with that illusion generation after generation take up their burden and march, because beyond the wilderness there must be a Promised Land into which some day some creatures unknown will enter. As though the evil of the past could be redeemed by any achievement of the future, or the perfection of one make up for the irremediable failure of another!

"Such ideas have only to be stated for their ab-

surdity to be palpable. Yet none the less they hold
men. Why? I cannot tell. I only know that they do
not and cannot hold me; that I look like a stranger
from another world upon the business of this one;
that I am among you, but not of you; that your
motives and aims to me are utterly unintelligible;
that you can give no account of them to which I
can attach any sense; that I have no clue to the
enigma you seem so lightly to solve by your religion, your philosophy, your science; that your
hopes are not mine, your ambitions not mine, your
principles not mine; that I am shipwrecked, and
see around me none but are shipwrecked too;
yet, that these, as they cling to their spars, call
them good ships and true, speak bravely of the
harbour to which they are prosperously sailing, and
even as they are engulfed, with their last breath,
cry, 'lo, we are arrived, and our friends are
waiting on the quay!' Who, under these circumstances is mad? Is it I? Is it you? I can only drift
and wait. It may be that beyond these waters there
is a harbour and a shore. But I cannot steer for it,
for I have no rudder, no compass, no chart. You
say you have. Go on, then, but do not call to me. I

must sink or swim alone. And the best for which I can hope is speedily to be lost in the silent gulf of oblivion. "

OFTEN as I had heard Audubon express these sentiments before, I had never known him to reveal so freely and so passionately the innermost bitterness of his soul. There was, no doubt, something in the circumstances of the time and place that prompted him to this personal note. For it was now the darkest and stillest hour of the night; and we sat in the dim starlight, hardly seeing one another, so that it seemed possible to say, as behind a veil, things that otherwise it would have been natural to suppress. A long silence followed Audubon's last words. They went home, I daresay to many of us more than we should have cared to confess. And I felt some difficulty whom to choose of the few who had not yet spoken, so as to avoid, as far as possible, a tone that would jar upon our mood. Finally, I selected Coryat, the poet, knowing he was incapable of a false note, and hoping he might perhaps begin to pull us, as it were, up out of the pit into which we had slipped. He responded from the darkness, with the hesitation and incoherence which, in him, I have always found so charming.

"I don't know," he began, "of course — well, yes, it may be all very bad — at least for some people. But I don't believe it is. And I doubt whether Audubon really — well, I ought n't to say that, I suppose. But anyhow, I 'm sure most people don't agree with him. At any rate, for my part, I find life extraordinarily good, just as it is, not mine only, I mean, but everybody's; well, except Audubon's, I suppose I ought to say, and even he, perhaps finds it rather good to be able to find it so bad. But I 'm not going to argue with him, because I know it 's no use. It 's all the other people I want to quarrel with — except Ellis, who has I believe some idea of the things that really count. But I don't think Allison has, or Wilson, or most of the people who talk about progress. Because, if you project, so to speak, all your goods into the future, that shows that you don't appreciate those that belong to life just as it is and wherever it is. And there must, I am sure, be something wrong about a view that makes the past and the present merely a means to the future. It 's as though one were to take a bottle and turn it upside down, emptying the wine out without noticing it; and then plan how tremendously one will improve the shape of the bottle. Well, I 'm not interested in the shape of bottles. And I am interested in wine. And — which is the point — I know that the wine is always there. It was there in the past, it 's here in the present, and it will be there in the future; yes, in spite of you all!" He flung this out with a kind of defiance that made us laugh. Whereupon he paused, as if he had done something indiscreet, and then after looking in vain for a bridge to take him across to his next starting place, decided, as it seemed, to jump, and went on as follows: "There 's Wilson, for instance, tells us that the new generation have 'no use for' — I don't know that he used that dreadful phrase, but that 's what he meant — that they have 'no use for' the Greeks, or the Romans, or the Middle Ages, or the eighteenth century, or anything but themselves. Well, I can only say I'm very sorry for them, and very glad I 'm not one of them. Why, just think of the extraordinary obliquity, or rather blindness of it! Because you don't agree with Plato, or Marcus Aurelius, or Saint Francis, you think

they 're only fit for the ash-heap. You might as
well say you would n't drink any wine except what
was made to-day! The literature and art of the past
can never be dead. It 's the flask where the geni of
life is imprisoned; you 've only to open it and the
life is yours. And what life! That it 's different
from ours is just its merit. I don't mean that it 's
necessarily better; but it preserves for us the things
we have dropped out. Because we, no more than
the men of the past, exhaust all the possibilities.
The whole wonderful drama of life is unfolded in
time, and we of this century are only one scene of
it; not the most passionate either or the most ab-
sorbing. As actors, of course, we 're concerned only
with this scene. But the curious thing is, we 're
spectators, too, or can be if we like. And from the
spectator's point of view, many of the episodes in
the past are much more interesting, if not more important, than those of the present. I mean, it
seems to me so stupid — I ought n't to say
stupid, I suppose, because of course you are n't
exactly — " Whereat we laughed again, and
he pulled himself up. " What I mean is, that to
take the philosophy or the religion of the past

and put it into your laboratory and test it for truth, and throw it away if it does n't answer the test, is to misconceive the whole value and meaning of it. The real question is, what extraordinary, fascinating, tragic or comic life went to produce this precious specimen? What new revelation does it give of the possibilities of the world? That's how you look at it, if you have the sense of life. You feel after life everywhere. You love it when you touch it. You ask it no questions about being good or bad. It just is, and you are akin to it. Fancy, for instance, a man being able to walk through the British Museum and pass the frieze of the Parthenon, and say he has no use for it! And why? Because, I suppose, we don't dress like that now, and can't ride horses bareback. Well, so much the worse for us! But just think! There, shrieking from the wall — no, I ought to say singing with the voice of angels — is the spirit of life in its loveliest, strongest, divinest incarnation, saying 'love me, understand me, be like me!' And the new generation passes by with its nose in the air sniffing, 'No! You 're played out! You did n't know science. And you did n't produce four children a-piece, as we mean to. And your education was rhetorical, and your philosophy absurd, and your vices — oh, unmentionable! No, no, young men! Not for us, thank you!' And so they stalk on, don't you see them, with their rational costume, and their rational minds, and their hard little hearts, and the empty place where their imagination ought to be! Dreadful, dreadful! Or perhaps they go, say, to Assisi, and Saint Francis comes to talk to them. And 'Look,' he says, 'what a beautiful world, if you 'd only get rid of your encumbrances! Money, houses, clothes, food, it 's all so much obstruction! Come and see the real thing; come and live with the life of the soul, burn like a flame, blossom like a flower, flow like a mountain stream!' 'My dear sir,' they reply, 'you 're unclean, impudent and ignorant! Moreover you 're encouraging mendicancy and superstition. Not to-day, thank you!' And off they go to the Charity Organization Committee. It 's — it 's — " He pulled himself up again, and then went on more quietly. "Well, one ought n't to get angry, and I daresay I 'm misrepresenting everybody. Besides, I have n't said exactly what I wanted to say. I

wanted to say — what was it? Oh, yes! that this
kind of attitude is bound up with the idea of progress. It comes of taking all the value out of the
past and present, in order to put it into the future.
And then you *don't* put it there! You can't! It
evaporates somehow, in the process. Where is it
then? Well, I believe it 's always there, in life, and
in every kind of life. It 's there all the time, in all
the things you condemn. Of course the things really are bad that you say are bad. But they 're so
good as well! I mean — well, the other day I read
one of those dreadful articles — at least, of course
they 're very useful I suppose — about the condition of the agricultural labourer. Well, then I took
a ride in the country, and saw it all in its setting
and complete, with everything the article had left
out; and it was n't so bad after all. I don't mean to
say it was all good either, but it was just wonderful. There were great horses with shaggy fetlocks
resting in green fields, and cattle wading in shallow
fords, and streams fringed with willows, and little
cheeping birds among the reeds, and larks and
cuckoos and thrushes. And there were orchards
white with blossom, and little gardens in the sun,

and shadows of clouds brushing over the plain.
And the much-discussed labourer was in the midst
of all this. And he really was n't an incarnate
grievance! He was thinking about his horses, or his
bread and cheese, or his children squalling in the
road, or his pig and his cocks and hens. Of course I
don't suppose he knew how beautiful everything
was; but I 'm sure he had a sort of comfortable
feeling of being a part of it all, of being somehow
all right. And he was n't worrying about his condition, as you all worry for him. I don't mean you
are n't right to worry, in a way; except that no one
ought to worry. But you ought n't to suppose it 's
all a dreadful and intolerable thing, just because
you can imagine something better. That, of
course, is only one case; but I believe it 's the same
everywhere; yes, even in the big cities, which, to
my taste, look from outside much more repulsive
and terrible. There 's a quality in the inevitable
facts of life, in making one's living, and marrying
and producing children, in the ending of one and
the beginning of another day, in the uncertainties
and fears and hopes, in the tragedies as well as the
comedies, something that arrests and interests and

absorbs, even if it does n't delight. I 'm not saying people are happy; sometimes they are and sometimes they are n't. But anyhow they are interested. And life itself is the interest. And that interest is perennial, and of all ages and all classes. And if you leave it out you leave out the only thing that counts. That 's why ideals are so empty; just because, I mean, they don't exist. And I assure you — now I 'm going to confess — that often, when I come away from some meeting or from reading some dreadful article on social reform, I feel as if I could embrace everything and every one I come across, simply for being so good as to exist — the 'bus-drivers, the cabmen, the shop-keepers, the slum-landlords, the slum-victims, the prostitutes, the thieves. There they are, anyhow, in their extraordinary setting, floating on the great river of life, that was and is and will be, itself its own justification, through whatever country it may flow. And if you don't realize that — if you have a whole community that does n't realize it — then, however happy and comfortable and equitable and all the rest of it you make your society, you have n't really done much for them. Their last state may even be worse than the first, because they will have lost the natural instinctive acceptance of life, without learning how to accept it on the higher plane.

" And that is why — now comes what I really do care about, and what I 've been wanting to say — that is why there is nothing so important for the future or the present of the world as poetry. Allison, for instance, and Wilson would be different men if only they would read my works! I 'm not sure even, if I may say so, that Remenham himself would n't be the better." Remenham, however, smilingly indicated that he had read them. Whereat Coryat rather comically remarked, " Oh, well! Yes! Perhaps then my poetry is n't quite good enough. But there 's Shakspere, and Milton, and — I don't care who it is, so long as it has the essential of all great poetry, and that is to make you feel the worth of things. I don't mean by that the happiness, but just the extraordinary value, of which all these unsolved questions about Good and Evil are themselves part. No one, I am sure, ever laid down a great tragedy — take the most terrible of all, take ' Lear ' — without an overwhelming sense of the value of life; life as it is, life at its most piti-

less and cruel, with all its iniquities, suffering, perplexity; without feeling he would far rather have
lived and had all that than not have lived at all.
But tragedy is an extreme case. In every simpler
and more common case the poet does the same
thing for us. He shows us that the lives he touches
have worth, worth of pleasure, of humour, of patience, of wisdom painfully acquired, of endur-
ance, of hope, even I will say of failure and despair.
He does n't blink anything, he looks straight at
it all, but he sees it in the true perspective, under a
white light, and seeing all the Evil says nevertheless
with God, 'Behold, it is very good.' You see," he
added, with his charming smile, turning to Audubon, "I agree with God, not with you. And perhaps if you were to read poetry . . . but, you
know, you must not only read it; you 've got to
feel it."

"Ah, said Audubon, "but that I 'm afraid is the
difficulty."

"I suppose it is. Well — I don't know that I can
say any more."

And without further ado he dropped back into
his seat.

SITTING next to Coryat was a man who had not for a long time been present at our meetings. His name was Harington. He was a wealthy man, the head of a very ancient family; and at one time had taken a prominent part in politics. But, of late, he had resided mainly in Italy devoting himself to study and to the collection of works of art. I did not know what his opinions were, for it so happened that I had never heard him speak or had any talk with him. I had no idea, therefore, when I called upon him, what he would be likely to say, and I waited with a good deal of curiosity as he stood a few moments silent. It was now beginning to get light, and I could see his face, which was unusually handsome and distinguished. He had indeed the air of a seventeenth century nobleman, and might, except for the costume, have stepped out of a canvas of Van Dyck. Presently he spoke in a rich mellow voice and with a gravity that harmonized with his bearing.

"Let me begin with a confession, perhaps I ought even to say an apology. To be among you again after so many years is a privilege; but it is one which brings with it elements of embarrassment. I have lived so long in a foreign land that I feel myself an alien here. I hear voices familiar of old, but I have forgotten their language; I see forms once well-known, but the atmosphere in which they move seems strange. I am fresh from Italy; and England comes upon me with a shock. Even her physical aspect I see as I never saw it before. I find it lovely, with a loveliness peculiar and unique. But I miss something to which I have become accustomed in the south; I miss light, form, greatness, and breadth. Instead, there is grey or golden haze, blurred outlines, tender skies, lush luxurious greenery. Italy rings like metal; England is a muffled drum. The one has the ardour of Beauty; the other the charm of the Picturesque. I dwell upon this because I seem to see — perhaps I am fanciful — a kindred distinction between the north and the south in quality of mind. The Greek intelligence, and the Italian, is pitiless, searching, white as the Mediterranean sunshine; the English and German is kindly, discreet, amiably and tenderly confused. The one blazes naked in a brazen sky; the other is tempered by vapours of sentiment. The English, in particular, I think, seldom make a

serious attempt to face the truth. Their prejudices
and ideals shut them in, like their green hedges;
and they live, even intellectually, in a country of
little fields. I do not deny that this is soothing and
restful; but I feel it — shall I confess — intoler-
ably cooping. I long for the searching light, the
wide prospect; for the vision of things as they really are. I have consorted too long with Aristotle and
Machiavelli to find myself at home in the country
of the Anglican Church and of Herbert Spencer."
Here he paused, and seemed to hesitate, while we
wondered what he could be leading up to. Then,
resuming, "This may seem," he went on, "a long
introduction; but it is not irrelevant; though I feel
some hesitation in applying it. But, if the last
speaker will permit me to take my text from him, I
would ask him, is it not a curiously indiscriminate
procedure to affirm indifferently value in all life? A
poet surely — and Coryat's practice, if he will allow me to say so, is sounder than his theory — a
poet seeks to render, wherever he can find it, the exquisite, the choice, the distinguished and the rare.
Not life, but beauty is his quest. He does not reproduce Nature, he imposes upon her a standard. And

so it is with every art, including the art of life itself. Life as such is neither good nor bad, and Audubon's undistinguishing censure is surely as much out of place as Coryat's undistinguishing approval. Life is raw material for the artist, whether he be the private man carrying out his own destiny, or the statesman shaping that of a nation. The end of the artist in either case is the good life; and on his own conception of that will depend the value of his work.

"I recall to your minds these obvious facts, at the risk of being tedious, because to-night, seeing the turn that our discussion has taken, we must regard ourselves as statesmen, or as would-be statesmen. And I, in that capacity, finding myself in disagreement with everybody, except perhaps Cantilupe, and asking myself the reason why, can only conclude that I have a different notion of the end to be pursued, and of the means whereby it can be attained. All of you, I think, except Cantilupe, have assumed that the good life, whatever it may be, can be attained by everybody; and that society should be arranged so as to secure that result. That is, in fact, the democratic postulate, which is now so generally accepted not only in this company but in the world at large. But it is that postulate that I dispute. I hold that the good life must either be the privilege of a few, or not exist at all. The good life in my view, is the life of a gentleman. That word, I know, has been degraded; and there is no more ominous sign of the degradation of the English people. But I use it in its true and noble sense. I mean by a gentleman a man of responsibility; one who because he enjoys privileges recognizes duties; a landed proprietor who is also, and therefore, a soldier and a statesman; a man with a natural capacity and a hereditary tradition to rule; a member, in a word, of a governing aristocracy. Not that the good life consists in governing; but only a governing class and those who centre round them are capable of the good life. Nobility is a privilege of the nobleman, and nobility is essential to goodness. We are told indeed, that Good is to be found in virtue, in knowledge, in art, in love. I will not dispute it; but we must add that only a noble man can be virtuous greatly, know wisely, perceive and feel finely. And virtue that is mean, knowledge that is pedantic, art that is base, love that is sensual are not Goods at all. A noble man of necessity feels and expresses himself nobly. His speech is literature, his gesture art, his action drama, his affections music. About him centres all that is great in literature, science, art. Magnificent buildings, exquisite pictures, statues, poems, songs, crowd about his habitation and attend him from the cradle to the grave. His fine intelligence draws to itself those of like disposition. He seeks genius, but he shuns pedantry; for his knowledge is part of his life. All that is great he instinctively apprehends, because it is akin to himself. And only so can anything be truly apprehended. For every man and every class can only understand and practise the virtues appropriate to their occupations. A professor will never be a hero, however much he reads the classics. A shop-walker will never be a poet, however much he reads poetry. If you want virtue, in the ancient sense, the sense of honour, of courage, of self-reliance, of the instinct to command, you must have a class of gentlemen. Otherwise virtue will be at best a mere conception in the head, a figment of the brain, not a character and a force. Why is the teaching of the classics now discredited

among you? Not because it is not as valuable as
ever it was, but because there is no one left to understand its value. The tradesmen who govern you
feel instinctively that it is not for them, and they
are right. It is above and beyond them. But it was
the natural food of gentlemen. And the example
may serve to illustrate the general truth, that you
cannot revolutionize classes and their relations
without revolutionizing culture. It is idle to suppose you can communicate to a democracy the
heritage of an aristocracy. You may give them
books, show them pictures, offer them examples.
In vain! The seed cannot grow in the new soil. The
masses will never be educated in the sense that the
classes were. You may rejoice in the fact, or you
may regret it; but at least it should be recognized.
For my own part I regret it, and I regret it because
I conceive that the good life is the life of the
gentleman.

"From this it follows that my ideal of a polity is
aristocratic. For a class of gentlemen presupposes
classes of workers to support it. And these, from
the ideal point of view, must be regarded as mere
means. I do not say that that is just; I do not say it

is what we should choose; but I am sure it is the
law of the world in which we live. Through the
whole realm of nature every kind exists only to be
the means of supporting life in another. Everywhere the higher preys upon the lower; everywhere the Good is parasitic on the Bad. And as in
nature, so in human society. Read history with an
impartial mind, read it in the white light, and you
will see that there has never been a great civilization that was not based upon iniquity. Those who
have eyes to see have always admitted, and always
will, that the greatest civilization of Europe was
that of Greece. And of that civilization not merely
an accompaniment but the essential condition was
slavery. Take away that and you take away Peri-
cles, Phidias, Sophocles, Plato. Dismiss Greece, if
you like. Where then will you turn ? To the Middle
Ages ? You encounter feudalism and serfdom. To
the modern world ? You run against wage-labour.
Ah, but, you say, we look to the future. We shall
abolish wage-labour, as we have abolished slavery.
We shall have an equitable society in which everybody will do productive work, and nobody will live
at the cost of others. I do not know whether you

can do this; it is possible you may; but I ask you to count the cost. And first let me call your attention to what you have actually done during the course of the past century. You have deposed your aristocracy and set up in their place men who work for their living, instead of for the public good, merchants, bankers, shop-keepers, railway directors, brewers, company-promoters. Whether you are better and more justly governed I do not pause to enquire. You appear to be satisfied that you are. But what I see, returning to England only at rare intervals, and what you perhaps cannot so easily see, is that you are ruining all your standards. Dignity, manners, nobility, nay, common honesty itself, is rapidly disappearing from among you. Every time I return I find you more sordid, more petty, more insular, more ugly and unperceptive. For the higher things, the real goods, were supported and sustained among you by your class of gentlemen, while they deserved the name. But by depriving them of power you have deprived them of responsibility, which is the salt of privilege; and they are rotting before your eyes, crumbling away and dropping into the ruck. Whether the general level of your civilization is rising I do not pronounce. I do not even think the question of importance; for any rise must be almost imperceptible. The salient fact is that the pinnacles are disappearing; that soon there will be nothing left that seeks the stars. Your middle classes have no doubt many virtues; they are, I will presume, sensible, capable, industrious, and respectable. But they have no notion of greatness, nay, they have an instinctive hatred of it. Whatever else they may have done, they have destroyed all nobility. In art, in literature, in drama, in the building of palaces or villas, *nihil tetigerunt quod non fœdaverunt*. Such is the result of entrusting power to men who make their own living, instead of to a class set apart by hereditary privilege to govern and to realize the good life. But, you may still urge, this is only a temporary stage. We still have a parasitic class, the class of capitalists. It is only when we have got rid of them, that the real equality will begin, and with it will come all other excellence. Well, I think it possible that you might establish, I will not say absolute equality, but an equality far greater than the world has ever seen; that you might exact from everybody some kind of productive work, in return for the guarantee of a comfortable livelihood. But there is no presumption that in that way you will produce the nobility of character which I hold to be the only thing really good. For such nobility, as all history and experience clearly shows, if we will interrogate it honestly, is the product of a class-consciousness. Personal initiative, personal force, a freedom from sordid cares, a sense of hereditary obligation based on hereditary privilege, the consciousness of being set apart for high purposes, of being one's own master and the master of others, all that and much more goes to the building up of the gentleman; and all that is impossible in a socialistic state. In the eternal order of this inexorable world it is prescribed that greatness cannot grow except in the soil of iniquity, and that justice can produce nothing but mediocrity. That the masses should choose justice at the cost of greatness is intelligible, nay it is inevitable; and that choice is the inner meaning of democracy. But gentlemen should have had the insight to see, and the courage to affirm, that the price was too great to pay. They did not; and the penalty is that they

are ceasing to exist. They have sacrificed themselves to the attempt to establish equity. But in that
attempt I can take no interest. The society in which
I believe is an aristocratic one. I hold, with Plato
and Aristotle, that the masses ought to be treated as
means, treated kindly, treated justly, so far as the
polity permits, but treated as subordinate always
to a higher end. But your feet are set on the other
track. You are determined to abolish classes; to
level down in order to level up; to destroy superiorities in order to raise the average. I do not say
you will not succeed. But if you do, you will realize
comfort at the expense of greatness, and your society will be one not of men but of ants and bees.

"For Democracy—note it well—destroys greatness in every kind, of intellect, of perception, as
well as of character. And especially it destroys art,
that reflection of life without which we cannot be
said to live. For the artist is the rarest, the most
choice of men. His senses, his perception, his intelligence have a natural and inborn fineness and distinction. He belongs to a class, a very small, a very
exclusive one. And he needs a class to appreciate
and support him. No democracy has ever pro-

duced or understood art. The case of Athens is wrongly adduced; for Athens was an aristocracy under the influence of an aristocrat at the time the Parthenon was built. At all times Art has been fostered by patrons, never by the people. How should they foster it? Instinctively they hate it, as they hate all superiorities. It was not Florence but the Medici and the Pope that employed Michelangelo; not Milan but Ludovic the Moor that valued Lionardo. It was the English nobles that patronized Reynolds and Gainsborough; the darlings of our middle class are Herkomer and Collier. There have been poets, it is true, who have been born of the people and loved of them; and I do not despise poetry of that kind. But it is not the great thing. The great thing is Sophocles and Virgil, a fine culture wedded to a rich nature. And such a marriage is not accomplished in the fields or the market-place. The literature loved by democracy is a literature like themselves; not literature at all, but journalism, gross, shrieking, sensational, base. So with the drama, so with architecture, so with every art. Substitute the mass for the patron, and you eliminate taste. The artist perishes; the charlatan survives and flourishes. Only in science have you still an aristocracy. For the crowd sees that there is profit in science, and lets it go its way. Because of the accident that it can be applied, it may be disinterestedly pursued. And democracy hitherto, though impatiently, endures an ideal aim in the hope of degrading its achievement to its own uses.

"Such being my view of democratic society I look naturally for elements that promise not to foster, but to counteract it. I look for the germs of a new aristocracy. They are hard to discover, and perhaps my desires override my judgment. But I fancy that it will be the very land that has suffered most acutely from the disease that will be the first to discover the remedy. I endorse Ellis's view of American civilization; but I allow myself to hope that the reaction is already beginning. I have met in Italy young Americans with a finer sense of beauty, distinction, and form, than I have been able to find among Englishmen, still less among Italians. And once there is cast into that fresh and unencumbered soil the seed of the ideal that made Greece great, who can prophecy into what forms of

beauty and thought it may not flower? The Plutocracy of the West may yet be transformed into an
Aristocracy; and Europe re-discover from America
the secret of its past greatness. Such, at least, appears to me to be the best hope of the world; and
to the realization of that hope I would have all men
of culture all the world over write their efforts.
For the kingdom of this earth, like that of heaven,
is taken by violence. We must work not with, but
against tendencies, if we would realize anything
great; and the men who are fit to rule must have
the courage to assume power, if ever there is to
be once more a civilization. Therefore it is that I,
the last of an old aristocracy, look across the Atlantic for the first of the new. And beyond socialism,
beyond anarchy, across that weltering sea, I strain
my eyes to see, pearl-grey against the dawn, the
new and stately citadel of Power. For Power is
the centre of crystallization for all good; given
that, you have morals, art, religion; without it, you
have nothing but appetites and passions. Power
then is the condition of life, even of the life of the
mass, in any sense in which it is worth having.
And in the interest of Democracy itself every

good Democrat ought to pray for the advent of Aristocracy."

ALL of our company had now spoken except two. One was the author, Vivian, and him I had decided to leave till the last. The other was John Woodman, a member of the Society of Friends, and one who was commonly regarded as a crank, because he lived on a farm in the country, worked with his hands, and refused to pay taxes on the ground that they went to maintain the army and navy. If Harington was handsome, Woodman was beautiful, but with beauty of expression rather than of features. I had always thought of him as a perfect example of that rare type, the genuine Christian. And since Harington had just revealed himself as a typical Pagan, I felt glad of the chance which brought the two men into such close juxtaposition. My only doubt was, whether Woodman would consent to speak. For, on previous occasions I had known him to refuse; and he was the only one of us who had always been able to sustain his refusal, without unpleasantness, but without yielding. To-night, however, he rose in response to my appeal, and spoke as follows:

" All the evening I have been wondering when the lot would fall on me, and whether, when it did, I should feel, as we Friends say, ' free ' to answer the call. Now that it has come, I am, I think, free; but not, if you will pardon me, for a long or eloquent speech. What I have to say I shall say as simply and as briefly as I can; and you, I know will listen with your accustomed tolerance, though I shall differ even more, if possible, from all the other speakers, than they have differed from one another. For you have all spoken from the point of view of the world. You have put forward proposals for changing society and making it better. But you have relied, for the most part, on external means to accomplish such changes. You have spoken of extending or limiting the powers of government, of socialism, of anarchy, of education, of selective breeding. But you have not spoken of the Spirit and the Life, or not in the sense in which I would wish to speak of them. MacCarthy, indeed, I remember, used the words ' the life of the spirit. ' But I could not well understand what he meant, except that he hoped to attain it by violence; and in that way what I would seek and value cannot be furthered. Coryat, again, and Harington spoke of the good life. But Coryat seemed to think that any and all life is good. The line of division which I see everywhere he did not see at all, the line between the children of God and the children of this world. I could not say with him that there is a natural goodness in life as such; only that any honest occupation will be good if it be practised by a good man. It is not wealth that is needed, nor talents, nor intellect. These things are gifts that may be given or withheld. But the one thing needful is the spirit of God, which is given freely to the poor and the ignorant who seek it. Believing this, I cannot but disagree, also, with Harington. For the life of which he spoke is the life of this world. He praises power, and wisdom, and beauty, and the excellence of the body and the mind. In these things, he says, the good life consists. And since they are so rare and difficult to attain, and need for their fostering, natural aptitudes, and leisure and wealth and great position, he concludes that the good life is possible only for the few; and that to them the many should be ministers. And if the goods he speaks of be really such, he is right; for in the things of the world, what one takes, another must resign. If there are rulers there must be subjects; if there are rich, there must be poor; if there are idle men there must be drudges. But the real Good is not thus exclusive. It is open to all; and the more a man has of it the more he gives to others. That Good is the love of God, and through the love of God the love of man. These are old phrases, but their sense is not old; rather it is always new, for it is eternal. Now, as of old, in the midst of science, of business, of invention, of the multifarious confusion and din and hurry of the world, God may be directly perceived and known. But to know Him is to love Him, and to love Him is to love his creatures, and most all of our fellow-men, to whom we are nearest and most akin, and with and by whom we needs must live. And if that love were really spread abroad among us, the questions that have been discussed to-night would resolve themselves. For there would be a rule of life generally observed and followed; and under it the conditions that make the problems would disappear. Of such a rule, all men, dimly and at moments, are aware. By it they were warned that slavery was wrong. And had they but read it more truly, and followed it more faithfully, they would never have made war to abolish what they would never have wished to maintain. And the same rule it is that is warning us now that it is wrong to fight, wrong to heap up riches, wrong to live by the labour of others. As we come to heed the warning we shall cease to do these things. But to change institutions without changing hearts is idle. For it is but to change the subjects into the rulers, the poor into the rich, the drudges into the idle men. And, as a result, we should only have idle men more frivolous, rich men more hard, rulers more incompetent. It is not by violence or compulsion, open or disguised, that the kingdom of heaven comes. It is by simple service on the part of those that know the law, by their following the right in their own lives, and preaching rather by their conduct than by their words.

"This would be a hard saying if we had to rely on ourselves. But we have God to rely on, who gives his help not according to the measure of our powers. A man cannot by taking thought add a cubit to his stature; he cannot increase the scope of his mind or the range of his senses; he cannot, by

willing, make himself a philosopher, or a leader of
men. But drawing on the source that is open to the
poorest and the weakest he can become a good
man; and then, whatever his powers, he will be
using them for God and man. If men do that, each
man for himself, by the help of God, all else will
follow. So true is it that if ye seek first the kingdom of heaven all these things shall be added unto
you. Yes, that is true. It is eternal truth. It does not
change with the doctrines of Churches nor depend
upon them. I would say even it does not depend on
Christianity. For the words would be true, though
there had never been a Christ to speak them.
And the proof that they are true is simply the direct witness of consciousness. We perceive such
truths as we perceive the sun. They carry with
them their own certainty; and on that rests the
certainty of God. Therein is the essence of all religion. I say it because I know. And the rest of you,
so it seems to me, are guessing. Nor is it, as it might
seem at first, a truth irrelevant to your discussion.
For it teaches that all change must proceed from
within outward. There is not, there never has
been, a just polity, for there has never been one

based on the love of God and man. All that you condemn — poverty, and wealth, idleness and excessive labour, squalor, disease, barren marriages, aggression and war, will continue in spite of all changes in form, until men will to get rid of them. And that they will not do till they have learnt to love God and man. Revolution will be vain, evolution will be vain, all uneasy turnings from side to side will be vain, until that change of heart be accomplished. And accomplished it will be in its own time. Everywhere I see it at work, in many ways, in the guise of many different opinions. I see it at work here to-night among those with whom I most disagree. I see it in the hope of Allison and Wilson, in the defiance of MacCarthy, in the doubt of Martin, and most of all in the despair of Audubon. For he is right to despair of the only life he knows, the life of the world whose fruits are dust and ashes. He drifts on a midnight ocean, unlighted by stars, and tossed by the winds of disappointment, sorrow, sickness, irreparable loss. Ah, but above him, if he but knew, as now in our eyes and ears, rises into a crystal sky the first lark of dawn. And the cuckoo sings, and the blackbird, do you not hear them? And the fountain rises ever from its fall in showers of silver sparks, up to the heaven it will not reach till fire has made it vapour. And so the whole creation aspires, out of the night of despair, into the cool freshness of dawn and on to the sun of noon. Let us be patient and follow each his path, waiting on the word of God till He be pleased to reveal it. For His way is not hard, it is joy and peace unutterable. And those who wait in faith He will bless with the knowledge of Himself. "

As he finished it was light, though the sun had not yet risen. The first birds were singing in the wood, and the fountain glistened and sang, and the plain lay before us like a bride waiting for the bridegroom. We were silent under the spell; and I scarcely know how long had passed before I had heart to call upon Vivian to conclude.

I HAVE heard Vivian called a philosopher, but the term is misleading. Those who know his writings — and they are too few — know that he concerned himself, directly or indirectly, with philosophic problems. But he never wrote philosophy; his methods were not those of logic;

and his sympathies were with science and the arts. In the early age of Greece he might have been Empedocles or Heraclitus; he could never have been Spinoza or Kant. He sought to interpret life, but not merely in terms of the intellect. He needed to see and feel in order to think. And he expressed himself in a style too intellectual for lovers of poetry, too metaphorical for lovers of philosophy. His Public, therefore, though devoted, was limited; but we, in our society, always listened to him with an interest that was rather enhanced than diminished by an element of perplexity. I have found it hard to reproduce his manner, in which it was clear that he took a conscious and artistic pleasure. Still less can I give the impression of his lean and fine-cut face, and the distinction of his whole personality. He stood up straight and tall against the whitening sky, and delivered himself as follows:

"Man is in the making; but henceforth he must make himself. To that point Nature has led him, out of the primeval slime. She has given him limbs, she has given him brain, she has given him the rudiment of a soul. Now it is for him to make or mar that splendid torso. Let him look no more to her for aid; for it is her will to create one who has the power to create himself. If he fail, she fails; back goes the metal to the pot; and the great process begins anew. If he succeeds, he succeeds alone. His fate is in his own hands.

"Of that fate, did he but know it, brain is the lord, to fashion a palace fit for the soul to inhabit. Yet still, after centuries of stumbling, reason is no more than the furtive accomplice of habit and force. Force creates, habit perpetuates, reason the sycophant sanctions. And so he drifts, not up but down, and Nature watches in anguish, self-forbidden to intervene, unless it be to annihilate. If he is to drive, and drive straight, reason must seize the reins; and the art of her driving is the art of Politics. Of that art, the aim is perfection, the method selection. Science is its minister, ethics its lord. It spares no prejudice, respects no habit, honours no tradition. Institutions are stubble in the fire it kindles. The present and the past it throws without remorse into the jaws of the future. It is the angel with the flaming sword swift to dispossess the crone that sits on her money-bags at Westminster.

"Or, shall I say, it is Hercules with the Augean stable to cleanse, of which every city is a stall, heaped with the dung of a century. With the Hydra to slay, whose hundred writhing heads of false belief, from old truth rotted into lies, spring inexhaustible fecund in creeds, interests, institutions. Of which the chief is Property, most cruel and blind of all, who devours us, ere we know it, in the guise of Security and Peace, killing the bodies of some, the souls of most, and growing ever fresh from the root, in forms that but seem to be new, until the root itself be cut away by the sword of the spirit. What that sword shall be called, socialism, anarchy, what you will, is small matter, so but the hand that wields it be strong, the brain clear, the soul illumined, passionate and profound. But where shall the champion be found fit to wield that weapon?

"He will not be found; he must be made. By Man Man must be sown. Once he might trust to Nature, while he was laid at her breast. But she has weaned him; and the promptings she no longer guides, he may not blindly trust for their issue. While she weeded, it was hers to plant; but

[154]

she weeds no more. He of his own will uproots or spares; and of his own will he must sow, if he would not have his garden a wilderness. Even now, precious plants perish before his eyes, even now weeds grow rank, while he watches in idle awe, and prates of his own impotence. He has given the reins to Desire, and she drives him back to the abyss. But harness her to the car, with reason for charioteer, and she will grow wings to waft him to his goal. That in him that he calls Love is but the dragon of the slime. Let him bury it in the grave of Self, and it will rise a Psyche, with wings too wide to shelter only the home. The Man that is to be comes at the call of the Man that is. Let him call then, soberly, not from the fumes of lust. For as is the call, so will be the answer.

"But for what should he call? For Pagan? For Christian? For neither, and for both. Paganism speaks for the men in Man, Christianity for the Man in men. The fruit that was eaten in Paradise, sown in the soul of man, bore in Hellas its first and fairest harvest. There rose upon the world of mind the triple sun of the Ideal. Aphrodite, born of the foam, flowered on the azure main, Tritons in her train and Nereids, under the flush of dawn. Apollo, radiant in hoary dew, leapt from the eastern wave, flamed through the heaven, and cooled his hissing wheels in the vaporous west. Athene, sprung from the brain of God, armed with the spear of truth, moved grey-eyed over the earth probing the minds of men. Love, Beauty, Wisdom, behold the Pagan Trinity! Through whose grace only men are men, and fit to become Man. Therefore, the gods are eternal; not they die, but we, when we think them dead. And no man who does not know them, and knowing, worship and love, is able to be a member of the body of Man. Thus it is that the sign of a step forward is a look backward; and Greece stands eternally at the threshold of the new life. Forget her, and you sink back, if not to the brute, to the insect. Consider the ant, and beware of her! She is there for a warning. In universal Anthood there are no ants. From that fate may men save Man!

"But the Pagan gods were pitiless; they preyed upon the weak. Their wisdom was rooted in folly, their beauty in squalor, their love in oppression. So fostered, those flowers decayed. And out of the

rotting soil rose the strange new blossoms we call
Faith, and Hope, and Charity. For Folly cried 'I
know not, but I believe;' Squalor, 'I am vile, but I
hope;' and the oppressed, 'I am despised, but I
love.' That was the Christian Trinity, the echo of
man's frustration, as the other was the echo of his
accomplishment. Yet both he needs. For because
he grows, he is dogged by imperfection. His weakness is mocked by those shining forms on the
mountain-top. But Faith, and Hope, and Charity
walk beside him in the mire, to kindle, to comfort
and to help. And of them justice is born, the plea of
the Many against the Few, of the nation against the
class, of mankind against the nation, of the future
against the present. In Christianity men were born
into Man. Yet in Him let not men die! For what
profits justice unless it be the step to the throne of
Olympus? What profit Faith and Hope without a
goal? Charity without an object? Vain is the love
of emmets, or of bees and coral-insects. For the
worth of love is as the worth of the lover. It is only
in the soil of Paganism that Christianity can come to
maturity. And Faith, Hope, Charity, are but seeds
of themselves till they fall into the womb of Wis-

dom, Beauty, and Love. Olympus lies before us, the snow-capped mountain. Let us climb it, together, if you will, not some on the corpses of the rest; but climb at least, not fester and swarm on rich meadows of equality. We are not for the valley, nor for the forests or the pastures. If we be brothers, yet we are brothers in a quest, needing our foremost to lead. Aphrodite, Apollo, Athene, are before us, not behind. Majestic forms, they gleam among the snows. March, then, men in Man!

"But is it men who attain? Or Man? Or not even He, but God? We do not know. We know only the impulse and the call. The gleam on the snow, the upward path, the urgent stress within, that is our certainty, the rest is doubt. But doubt is a horizon, and on it hangs the star of hope. By that we live; and the science blinds, the renunciation maims, that would shut us off from those silver rays. Our eyes must open, as we march, to every signal from the height. And since the soul has indeed 'immortal longings in her' we may believe them prophetic of their fruition. For her claims are august as those of man, and appeal to the same

witness. The witness of either is a dream; but such
dreams come from the gate of horn. They are
principles of life, and about them crystallizes the
universe. For will is more than knowledge, since
will creates what knowledge records. Science hangs
in a void of nescience, a planet turning in the dark.
But across that void Faith builds the road that
leads to Olympus and the eternal Gods. "

By the time he had finished speaking the sun
had risen, and the glamour of dawn was passing
into the light of common day. The birds sang
loud, the fountain sparkled, and the trees rustled
softly in the early breeze. Our party broke up
quietly. Some went away to bed; others strolled
down the gardens; and Audubon went off by ap-
pointment to bathe with my young nephew, as gay
and happy, it would seem, as man could be. I was
left to pace the terrace alone, watching the day
grow brighter, and wondering at the divers fates
of men. An early bell rang in the little church at
the park-gate; a motor-car hooted along the high-
way. And I thought of Cantilupe and Harington,
of Allison and Wilson, and beyond them of the
vision of the dawn and the daybreak, of Wood-

man, the soul, and Vivian, the spirit. I paused for a last look down the line of bright statues that bordered the long walk below me. I fancied them stretching away to the foot of Olympus; and without elation or excitement, but with the calm of an assured hope, I prepared to begin the new day.

THE END